AMERICA TRAVELS

Books by Alice Dalgliesh

THE LITTLE WOODEN FARMER
THE BLUE TEAPOT
AMERICA TRAVELS

Published by The Macmillan Company

AMERICA BEGINS
THE THANKSGIVING STORY
THE COLUMBUS STORY
THE FOURTH OF JULY STORY
THE BEARS ON HEMLOCK MOUNTAIN
THE COURAGE OF SARAH NOBLE
ADAM AND THE GOLDEN COCK

(and others)

Published by Charles Scribner's Sons

AMERICA TRAVELS

The Story of Travel in America

Revised Edition

By Alice Dalgliesh

Illustrated by Hildegard Woodward

New York The Macmillan Company 1962

Revised Edition

Second Printing 1962

Library of Congress catalog card number: 61–16542

The Macmillan Company, New York

Brett-Macmillan Ltd., Galt, Ontario

Printed in the United States of America

CONTENTS

Traveling Tales Page

Deborah Travels Alone 1

Hector Crosses the Atlantic 13

The Small Yellow Train 25

The Kitten on the Canal Boat 35

The Home on Wheels 45

New Shoes for Diamond 55

Mary Jane and the Buggy 63

Harvey and Higgins Incorporated 71

The Picture Story of Travel

Wheels and Horses 82

The Days of Sail 90

Steam 93

Traveling West 107

New Ways to Travel 115

Speed! 121

Jets—and the Space Age 127

AMERICA TRAVELS

INTRODUCTION

WE ARE standing on the sidewalk of one of the busiest avenues of New York. Traffic goes by so fast that we cannot cross the street, we must wait until the traffic light changes. How noisy it is! Autos and taxis go whizzing by. Here comes a long gray bus; it has come from another city. Farther down that street we can see a large railroad terminal. Trains are leaving and arriving every few minutes.

There goes a taxi on its way to the docks. A great steamship is sailing to-day, taking hundreds of people to Europe. In a few days they will be on the other side of the Atlantic.

Meanwhile from the big airports, airplanes and jets are leaving for places all over the world.

Automobiles, buses, trains, liners, jets! We are so accustomed to them we seldom stop to think that a little over a hundred years ago none of them existed. A great deal has happened in a very short time. If we go back in imagination through the years, we can find out how different things used to be.

DEBOROAH TRAVELS ALONE

WHICH IS THE STORY OF HOW DEBORAH
TRAVELED ALONE BY STAGECOACH

THIS HAPPENED IN NEW ENGLAND
IN THE YEAR 1820

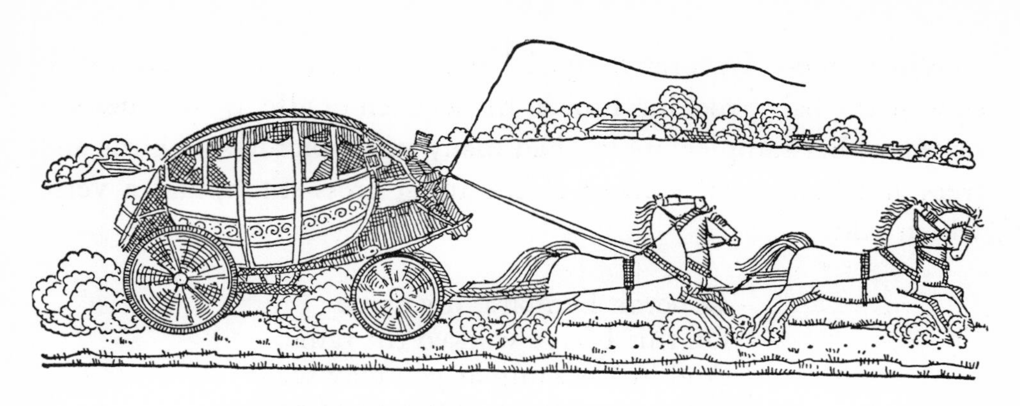

DEBORAH TRAVELS ALONE

ONCE upon a time, in the days when everything moved slowly, there was a little girl named Deborah. Deborah lived in a quiet white house in a quiet New England village.

The most exciting thing that happened in Deborah's village was the arrival of the stagecoach, which stopped at the tavern to change horses. Sometimes Deborah's father took her down to the tavern to see the coach come in and to see the four tired horses give place to four that were fresh and prancing, eager to start on the journey. Then the coachman with his tall hat and broad red sash climbed into his seat, took the reins, flourished his whip, and off went the stagecoach with all its passengers. Deborah wished she could go with it, but that could not be. In those days one had to have a real reason for traveling.

Nothing really exciting had ever happened to Deborah herself. On week days she went to school and read from dull little books with dull pictures. These books were full of stories about bad little girls and boys who were punished for their naughtiness and good children whom everyone loved.

After school Deborah helped her mother in the house or took care of the baby, rocking him in his wooden cradle. Sometimes she sewed on her sampler, which had many small pictures of birds and trees and flowers all worked in the finest cross-stitch, and a verse which said:

Deborah Fenton is my name
On this I have worked the same,
And by my sampler you may see
What care my parents took of me.

Deborah's parents *did* take care of her. They never let her go anywhere alone or do anything all by herself. At night when mother had warmed the bed with the big brass warming pan, had braided Deborah's hair, had helped her undress, and had seen to it that the windows were tightly closed, she kissed Deborah good night, blew out the candle and went softly out of the room. Then Deborah lay in the middle of the big bed, and played her favorite game of "suppose." The game went like this:

"Suppose Mother would let me go over to Truly Adams' house all by myself, to spend the day!"

"Suppose I could spend the *night!*"

"Suppose Mother would let me go to the store alone!"

"Suppose Father would let me go alone to see the coach come in!"

"*Suppose I could ride on the coach all by myself!*"

"*Suppose I could ride all the way to Boston!*"

At this point Deborah could think of nothing more, so she usually fell asleep. Sometimes she dreamed that she was traveling on the stagecoach. This was pleasant, though she never thought it could really and truly happen in broad daylight.

But it did. Deborah actually traveled by herself and went all the way to Boston! It seems very hard to believe, but this is how it happened.

One day a letter came from Deborah's aunt in Boston. Letters came so seldom and so slowly in those days that Mother was sure it must be bad news. Instead it was good news, though quite startling and surprising. Deborah's cousin Faith was to be married. Could Deborah and her parents come to the wedding?

"I have never been to a wedding, and I do so like my cousin Faith," said Deborah. "Can we go?"

"I am afraid not," said Mother. "Father cannot leave his work and I cannot leave baby. There would be no one to take you."

Deborah's heart beat so fast that it seemed to take her breath away. For a few minutes she said nothing. Then: "Mother, can't I go alone?"

The words tumbled out so quickly that Mother was quite sure she had not heard them aright.

"Deborah, *what* did you say?"

"Can't I go alone?"

"Child! The very idea!"

"But, Mother, I am eight years old. I know I could do it."

"I must talk it over with your father," said Mother, with a worried wrinkle between her eyes.

Father and Mother talked it over; Deborah listened. Father thought it was possible. Mother thought it was not. Deborah said it was the one thing in the world she wanted to do. She reminded them that after the wedding Faith was going such a distance, to Philadelphia, that none of them would see her again. The whole week was very sad.

At the end of the week Mother sighed and said that Deborah might go. Father said that children sometimes traveled alone and that the coachmen took good care of them. Mother could not help being worried about it for Boston was so far away, all of forty miles! It would take five or six hours to get there by coach. Deborah was glad that the journey would last so long.

The next two weeks were full of the most delightful preparations. The sturdy little pigskin trunk was brought down from the attic. Mother sewed and washed and ironed, and into the trunk went Deborah's belongings, including the beautiful new dress that was to be worn at the wedding. Mother gave many directions as she packed the trunk.

"Remember, Deborah, that these pantaloons are to wear with your blue dress."

"The white dress with the rosebuds is only for Sunday."

"Don't forget to take your tonic three times a day."

"Remember to go to bed early. You need your sleep."

"Eat everything that Aunt Ellen puts before you."

So it went, with Deborah listening dutifully to all the directions and wondering how she could possibly remember them all.

When the trunk was packed, and Deborah's best bonnet was in the bandbox, there were still the presents for Aunt Ellen, for Faith, and for Rachel who was just Deborah's age. They were such large presents that they would not fit in anywhere. There was a canary in a gilded cage, to take the place of Aunt Ellen's canary that had died some months ago. There was a china tea set for Faith and also a doll for Rachel. Deborah was glad that her own present for Faith was nothing larger than a pincushion.

It was a very handsome pincushion that she had worked herself, with a beautiful design of roses and a white dove.

The day came at last. With all her boxes and bundles Deborah stood waiting for the coach to start. Father was jolly and made jokes. Mother was nervous and wiped her eyes with her handkerchief. The horses were changed and it was time to get into the coach. Deborah stepped in. The coachman put the trunk at the back of the coach, and Father handed in the bundles. Fortunately there were only two passengers in the coach, an old lady who sat in one corner and an old gentleman who sat in the other and peered at Deborah over his spectacles. Deborah held the bird cage on her lap. The canary, much disturbed, gave little frightened calls.

"Ta-ra-ra! ta-ra-rah!" That was the horn, the signal that the coach was ready to leave. Mother and Father were telling the fat, red-faced coachman to be sure to look after Deborah.

"Take great care of her," begged Mother. "She is so little to travel alone."

"You need not worry, Madam," smiled the coachman. "I'll see the little lady safely to Boston." He gathered up the reins and suddenly the horses started forward, with a jerk that almost threw Deborah from her seat. The canary gave a shrill scream. Deborah held the cage more tightly and leaned forward to look out of the window. Father was waving and Mother waved whenever she did not need her handkerchief to dry her eyes. Deborah waved, feeling a little tearful herself. The old lady leaned forward and patted her knee, which made Deborah smile in a watery sort of way.

Now Mother and Father were out of sight. Even the slender white steeple of the church was hidden behind the trees. Deborah settled back in her seat. A strange warm little feeling of excitement crept over her. For the first time in her life she was doing something *all by herself!*

The coach rumbled on. The tears stopped coming into Deborah's eyes and she could see clearly once more. It was the fall of the year and tall elm trees met like a golden arch across the roads. Yellow leaves rustled under the horses' hooves, and floated down from the trees. The coachman cracked his whip and talked to his horses. "Git up there, Tom! Bob, you do your share of pulling! Easy there, Blackie!"

Now they were passing a small country schoolhouse. A group of little girls with calico sunbonnets and boys with no hats at all stood waiting to see the coach drive by. Deborah waved to them. The little girls dropped shy curtseys and the boys ducked their heads. The good-natured coachman threw them some peppermints and there was a general scramble. Soon the children were out of sight.

At the first town the coach stopped to take on more passengers and Deborah's bundles began to be very much in the way. She was squeezed into a corner, still holding the bird cage on her lap, while the old gentleman held the largest bundle. A pretty young lady held the box containing the tea set, while a young gentleman with brown whiskers held the bandbox and looked very foolish holding it. If Deborah had not been so little and pretty and gentle it is certain that the other passengers would have been a trifle cross. As it was they were very good natured indeed. Soon Deborah was telling them all about the wedding and Aunt Ellen's canary, besides explaining what was in each of the bundles.

For a time all went well. There had been heavy rains and the roads were muddy, but the coach rattled along at a good pace, stopping only to pay toll at a tollgate. Then, no one knew just how it happened, but there was a jerk, one wheel sank deep in the mud and the passengers were thrown in a heap. When they had scrambled back into their seats and were straightening hats and bonnets, the coachman looked in at the window.

"Drat that bird!" he said, for the canary was close to having a fit. "You'll have to get out, ladies. And the gentlemen will have to give us a hand or we'll be here all night."

The passengers climbed out. Deborah talked soothingly to the canary and wondered what her parents would say if they could see her now. The men pushed and pulled and groaned and grunted but the coach did not move. The wheel was sunk so deep in the mud that it would have to be dug out. Deborah and the ladies stood at the side of the road, a lonely country road with nothing in sight but mud, a few trees, and a single farmhouse. Raindrops began to fall, they splashed on Deborah's curls and on her new pelisse. Deborah shivered and sneezed.

"Dearie me!" said the old lady. "This is too bad. We should not be standing here permitting this sweet child to catch her death of cold. Perhaps that farmhouse will give us shelter."

So Deborah and the old lady and the pretty young lady picked their way through mud and dark-brown puddles to the farmhouse, and soon were seated before a warm, crackling fire in the big kitchen fireplace. The farmer's wife brought tea for the ladies and a glass of warm milk for Deborah. The farmer's little girl gazed shyly at the visitors from a distance. The big sheep dog rose from his place by the fire, walked over to Deborah and put his head on her lap. It was all very cozy and comfortable. When the coachman appeared at the door to say that they were ready to start, Deborah wished she could stay. It was none too warm in the coach and a long dreary road lay ahead. Who could tell what might happen?

Nothing serious *did* happen, though sometimes the road was too rough for comfort. In some places the coachman shouted, "To the right! Passengers lean to the right!" and everyone leaned to one side to keep the coach from turning over. Deborah held her breath until she was sure that everything was safe. They stopped at a roadside tavern for a meal, which had to be a hurried one because of the time that had been wasted.

At last the coach arrived safely in Boston. There was Aunt Ellen, a stout motherly person with a jolly smile. She did not even seem worried or disturbed because the coach was late.

"Well, here you are at last!" she cried. "To think of you traveling all alone!"

Deborah stepped out carefully, holding the bird cage in one hand. "Yes, I came all by myself," she said. Then the young gentleman got out and handed out the bundles, the tea set and the bandbox. Aunt Ellen's eyes grew big and round.

"All by yourself, indeed!" she said. "Well, well, all by yourself!" She laughed so heartily that Deborah joined in, though she had not the least idea what the joke was. The coach went on its way and Deborah stood by the boxes and bundles waving good-by to all her fellow travelers. She hoped the coach would not get stuck in the mud again. Perhaps it would be lighter now that she and all the bundles and boxes were out of it!

It was quite late when Deborah reached her aunt's home, and there was time only to open some of the presents, to find the canary a quiet place where he might recover from the excitement of the journey, and to have supper. Then Deborah and Rachel tried on

The coach was stuck in the mud.

the dresses they were to wear at the wedding and looked at themselves admiringly in the mirror.

"Who would ever think we were cousins!" said Rachel. "Your hair is so fair and mine is so dark."

"And you are fat, and I am thin," said Deborah.

"But we are both the same height—and I'm not really *fat*," said Rachel.

"Time for bed!" said Aunt Ellen. "You will have plenty of time for dresses in the morning. Deborah's mother would be horrified if she could see how late it is."

When Aunt Ellen had put out the candle and gone, not very softly, from the room, the two little girls lay in the big bed, still talking.

"You can't comb your own hair, can you?" said Rachel.

"No," said Deborah.

"Or unbutton your own dress?"

"No," said Deborah.

"Or do anything very much all by yourself?"

This was too much for Deborah. She sat bolt upright in bed.

"Why Rachel Fenton! This very day *I came all by myself on the coach to Boston!*"

Which left Rachel nothing at all to say.

HECTOR CROSSES THE ATLANTIC

WHICH IS THE STORY OF A STORMY
PASSAGE ON A SAILING VESSEL
ABOUT THE YEAR 1825

HECTOR CROSSES THE ATLANTIC

THERE was a great bustle and stir on the docks at Liverpool. The packet boat *Friendship* was almost ready to sail. There she lay, every sail in readiness but as yet none of them loosed. On the dock sat a little girl with a small scared lamb held closely to her. A tall sailor stopped to speak to them.

"Where are you going with the lamb, little lady?"

"To the States," said Jenny.

"Well now, to think of that!" chuckled the sailor. "And why do you have to take a lamb with you? Ain't there plenty of sheep in the States?"

"Hector is my pet lamb," said Jenny. "I couldn't possibly leave him behind. My mother was for leaving him but I could not do that."

"And what will the skipper of the *Friendship* say?"

"The captain is a friend of my father," said Jenny. "He said I could take Hector. We are going to my father in New York, he has a home for us there."

The sailor laughed and passed on.

Jenny's mother came hurrying up. "Are you tired of waiting, Jenny? I have had our trunks safely arranged for. Now it is time to go on board."

On the ship there was even more noise and bustle than on the dock. The deck seemed to be full of ropes and of hurrying sailors. Jenny found a safe corner where she could watch it all. Soon the anchor was weighed. The red-shirted sailors tramped around the capstan bar taking in slack on the ropes with which the *Friendship* was warping out of dock. These ropes were attached to buoys in the channel outside, and as they were hauled in by the windlass the ship was gradually moved out from the dock. The chantey man began a song and the sailors joined in the refrain. Tramp, tramp, tramp went their feet in tune to the song. Click, click, click went the capstan.

The longshoremen in their little boats cast the ropes loose from the buoys. Now for the sails! The sailors hauled on the ropes. The chantey man began his song.

"As I was walking down Paradise street"—
　　"*Way-ay blow the man down*" [answered the sailors].
"A brass-bound policeman I happened to meet"—
　　"*Give me some time to blow the man down.*"
"Says he, 'You're a blackballer by the cut of your hair,' "
　　"*Way-ay blow the man down.*"
" 'I know you're a blackballer by the clothes that you wear.' "
　　"*Give me time to blow the man down.*"

How the sailors roared the chorus! The big square sails caught the breeze and the *Friendship* moved slowly toward the open sea.

"Way-ay blow the man down!"

If the *Friendship* had been beautiful before she was far more beautiful now, clothed in white canvas from topmast to deck. On her large foresail was painted a big black ball to show that she belonged to the Black Ball Line. The coast of England was no longer to be seen. Jenny felt a little sad, but only a very little, for everything was so new and interesting.

"Oh, Mother, now we are really out at sea!"

"We shall surely be drowned," said her mother tearfully, "or perhaps we shall be captured by pirates."

"Nonsense!" said the captain, who had just come past and heard the conversation. "We'll have fair weather on this passage. As for pirates, they are seldom seen on the Atlantic in these days. Jenny, you can't keep the lamb with you all the time. There is a place for him with the other animals, and a lad who will take care of him. Here he is!"

Jenny looked up to see a young sailor with a shock of red hair and a pleasant, freckled face.

"This is Jim," said the captain. "Let him take Hector."

"I want to see where Hector goes," said Jenny. She and Hector followed Jim to the place where the animals were kept. It was a real deck farm. There in a small wooden house was the cow that would give fresh milk for the voyage. In smaller pens were sheep and pigs.

"Why," said Jenny, "if anything should happen to the ship how could we get into the boat? It's full of ducks and chickens!"

Jim laughed. The longboat had been roofed over and made a fine home for the chickens, who poked their heads out through the wire netting. It was very noisy, for all the animals were disturbed at finding themselves in such a strange place and they mooed and grunted, clucked and bleated and quacked.

"Do you think Hector will be safe here?" asked Jenny. "What if a wave should wash over the deck?"

"I'll take good care of him," promised Jim. So, with a final pat, Jenny left Hector with the other animals.

Pleasant days followed. The *Friendship* ran before the wind with all sails set. Jenny played on the deck and thought how easy it was to cross the Atlantic. Sometimes she visited Hector and found him well content with Jim to look after him. Once she visited the steerage passengers in their crowded, uncomfortable quarters. They slept in hard wooden bunks and cooked their own food. Jenny was glad that her meals, although they were not very good ones, were served at the long table in the saloon.

The thing that Jenny liked best of all was to watch the captain write in the big log book the story of all that happened on the voyage. She would kneel beside him as he wrote. "A light westerly breeze." That was only weather and not so interesting. But now—"To-day we passed the brig *Lucy*—" That was a different matter. "Draw the *Lucy*, please, Captain, draw the *Lucy*." Jenny watched, fascinated, as the captain sketched the brig, just as they had seen her. Jenny liked to turn back the pages to see pictures of other boats.

Then came the storm. The sky darkened so suddenly and the wind rose so rapidly that the sailors had scarcely time to take in sail. From

Where the animals lived.

the safe shelter of the deck house Jenny watched them climb the swaying rigging to struggle with the sails. The great canvas sails pulled and tugged and billowed like huge white birds trying to be free. The sky grew blacker. The sea was an ugly dark color and the *Friendship* no longer rode smoothly, but plunged and tossed. The captain gave the order, "All passengers below. Close the hatches," and Jenny and her mother found themselves almost prisoners in the tiny cabin. It was a *very* small cabin, full of strange smells and lighted only by an oil lantern that hung from the ceiling.

Those were terrible days. Jenny and her mother dared not move from their bunks for fear of being dashed against the walls. Great waves beat on the ship and she quivered from stem to stern. Sometimes she plunged so deeply between the waves that it seemed as though she would never come up again. Water came through the closed hatches and trickled into the cabin.

"I knew we would be drowned!" wept Jenny's mother. Occasionally the captain looked in at the door and spoke cheerfully. His oilskin coat dripped water and he looked pale and tired. Not a wink of sleep did he get, and these days there were no pictures in the log book.

The storm grew worse. Every board strained and creaked. It seemed as if the ship would go to pieces. Then came the most terrifying time of all when a sailor came into the cabin and fastened boards across the bunks to give Jenny and her mother something to which they could hold. The ship gave an extra lurch and the feeble, flickering lantern went out. The cabin was in darkness. Jenny lay holding tightly to the boards as the *Friendship* rolled and pitched. She tried to keep her mind on all the pleasant things she had known on land. As she lay in the darkness she could picture their homelike cottage with the garden full of flowers. Canterbury bells, columbine, sweet william, heart's ease, and hollyhock—the very names of the flowers were smooth and comforting. Jenny said them over and over. Then she thought of the wood full of pale gold primroses and of Hector frisking in the field near by. Poor Hector! Jenny wondered what had happened to him. Perhaps a wave had swept him overboard.

The ship gave a mighty plunge and the boards cracked like pistol shots. Jenny lay very still, saying under her breath, "Please make the waves get less and let us get safely to the States."

The waves did get less. Gradually the sea became calmer and the storm was over. Jenny staggered weakly up on deck to find the sea shining and the sky clear and blue. There was Jim, cleaning the brass on the railing.

"Jim," said Jenny, "where is Hector?"

Jim turned pale under his freckles. "I don't know, Missy."

"Don't know! Oh, Jim, you promised to take care of him!"

"Well, Missy, it's like this. It's my first voyage and in the storm I was sick as a dog. When I was better Hector was gone. A wave took the cows overboard, so there's no telling where the lamb is now."

"We must find him," said Jenny. All over the ship they searched, even in dark spots where rats brushed by them. At last a faint "Ba-a-a" led them to a far corner of the galley, the place where the coal for the cook stove was kept. There crouched the lamb, a frightened lamb black from nose to tail.

"Oh, Hector!" said Jenny. She threw her arms around him, regardless of black streaks on her dress.

"I'll scrub him, Missy," promised Jim.

It was probably the first time that a lamb had had a bath on board a vessel and all the crew were interested. They gathered around and offered many suggestions. Jenny sat on a coil of rope and watched. A large sailor held Hector while Jim poured pails of water over him and scrubbed vigorously. Hector curled back his lip. He bucked and snorted as the salt water got in his eyes. He bleated pitifully. But Jim went on scrubbing and soon the lamb, if not quite white, was at least a respectable pale gray. Then Jim tied a string around his neck, with a bell on it.

"Now, my fine fellow, I shall always know where you are," he said.

Days followed in which the *Friendship* sailed peacefully and Hector's bell tinkled gayly. Then for a week the winds were against them and the ship made scarcely any headway. Jenny thought this was very dull. The voyage was lengthening and the food was running low. There was little water left and that little was scarcely fit to drink. Jenny often went thirsty rather than drink the evil-tasting stuff. There was no milk since the cows had been lost overboard. At last the long weeks of the voyage were over and the *Friendship* sailed into New York harbor. Jenny stood on the deck to catch a first glimpse of the strange new country and of her father. They came within sight of the docks.

"Why are all those people here?" asked Jenny. "Have they all come to meet Mother and me?"

"Hardly!" laughed the captain. "I'll show you why they have come. They want the latest news from England."

The captain put a speaking trumpet to his lips and shouted the news to the waiting crowd. They cheered and shouted back. The

Friendship was alongside of the dock now and Jenny looked eagerly for her father.

"You'll see him soon enough," said the captain. "How do you like being a sailor, Jenny?"

"It's very pleasant," said Jenny, who by this time had quite forgotten the storm and all the hardships of the voyage. "Oh! there's my father!" She leaned over the rail and called, "Father! Father! Here we are, Mother and Hector and I—safely across the Atlantic! Look, Father! Here we are!"

THE SMALL YELLOW TRAIN

WHICH IS THE STORY OF HOW DAVID
WENT RIDING ON THE FIRST TRAIN
OF THE MOHAWK AND HUDSON RAILROAD

THIS HAPPENED IN NEW YORK STATE
IN THE YEAR 1831

THE SMALL YELLOW TRAIN

"DAVID," said Aunt Melissa, "there are times when I truly believe your questions will drive me crazy!"

"He's at it all day long," said Aunt Ann. "What makes the steam engine go, and how big is it, and what does it look like? I can't answer the questions. Why do folks want to bother their heads about those new-fangled affairs, anyway?"

"Why, indeed!" agreed Aunt Melissa.

David said nothing for a few minutes. He was sorry he had annoyed the aunts. They had been so kind to him since he had come to stay in their comfortable house. He would be with them until his father and mother came home from a long voyage in his father's ship. Perhaps he should not talk so much about the new locomotive, not even if all the town of Albany was still talking about it.

"I didn't mean—" said David.

"Neither did I," said Aunt Melissa, hastily.

"Well," suggested Aunt Ann, "I've heard there is a man in town who is showing a picture of the queer contraption. Perhaps if we took David to see it he would find the answers to some of his questions."

David sat up straight, his eyes shining.

"A good plan," said Aunt Melissa. "We'll go this very afternoon."

So, like most of the other people in Albany, the aunts and David went to see the picture. It was cut out of black paper and it had been made by a man who actually rode on the train the first time it carried passengers. Now he was showing a picture of it in his studio and charging a small admission fee.

As David came into the room he gave a little gasp. There was the picture, a big one, longer than David himself, all across the wall on one side of the room. Now he knew just how the train looked!

People were talking about the picture.

"It's wonderful!" they said. "Just like magic. Cut out of a piece of black paper with a pair of common scissors. And see the engineer! It's David Matthews himself, not quite as large as life, but twice as natural. The way Mr. Brown takes these likenesses is astonishing."

"David," said Aunt Melissa, "come here and let Mr. Brown cut your portrait."

David sighed as he left the picture of the train. All the time that Mr. Brown was cutting his portrait David kept his eyes on the little engine. Snip, snip went Mr. Brown's scissors. Small pieces of black paper fell to the floor. People stretched their necks and leaned over to watch what he was doing. Snip, snip, and the portrait was finished. Not nearly as large as life, but twice as natural!

It was hard to get David away from the picture of the train, he could have looked at it all day long.

"Now he will be satisfied," said Aunt Ann.

But David was not satisfied. He had a great many more questions to ask and he wanted to see the train with his own eyes. At last the day came when he found courage to tell the aunts that he wanted more than anything in the world to ride on the small yellow train. When he told them they were shocked. They were horrified. They were terrified.

"Have you heard the tales of what happened on the first trip?" they asked. "Why it jerked so that Sally Jones was thrown from her seat. Her father lost his hat and never did find it again!"

"And the sparks! Mrs. Burton had a big hole burned in her new dress. The ladies who were in the open cars had to put up parasols to keep the sparks and cinders off their clothes."

"Sally said her face was black from the smoke after they had ridden a while."

"It is a very remarkable invention, David, but a most dangerous and uncomfortable way to travel."

All this did not discourage David in the least. It simply made him wish more than ever that he could ride on the train. In fact he knew he would never be quite happy until he had done so.

The aunts knew this too. So, because they were really very fond of David, they began to talk in this way:

"He does so want to go," said Aunt Melissa.

"Perhaps it is not so bad after all. I hear they have made improvements."

"Sally Jones always makes things seem worse than they are."

"And Elizabeth has begged us to bring David to visit her in Schenectady."

"Do you think we might try it?"

David could scarcely believe his ears when the aunts told him they had decided to travel by the train. When the day came it was bright and sunny. It took quite a while to get ready. Both aunts wore their second-best silk dresses and David's hair was brushed to a remarkable neatness. The aunts had hired a carriage to drive to the place from which the train started. As this was David's especial day, he was allowed to ride in front with the coachman.

Aunt Melissa and Aunt Ann were safely settled in the carriage. The coachman cracked his whip. They were off! David braced his feet against the dashboard and looked sideways at the coachman. He looked solemn and cross, so David did not speak. There was silence for a long time. Then the coachman looked at David.

"Going to ride on the train, I hear?"

"Yes," said David.

"H'm," said the coachman. "More time than sense. What do folks want with them steam engines anyway, puffing and snorting and scaring the horses half out of their wits? Thirty miles an hour it goes! I say no good will come of people shooting around the country like skyrockets. Give me horses!"

"But it's a very wonderful invention," ventured David.

"H'm!" said the coachman. "That may be. But did you hear about the steam locomotive that blew up down Charleston way? Folks scattered all over the tracks. Horses for me!"

David could think of nothing to say. He hoped Aunt Ann and Aunt Melissa had not heard the conversation, for there was still time to turn back. Now they were at the place from which the train started. There was a steep hill leading into the town, and people thought that engines could run only on level ground. So there was a little car on which passengers sat while a stationary engine pulled them up to the top of the hill. The aunts did not care for this at all.

The car reached the top of the slope. The passengers stepped off —and there was the *De Witt Clinton* engine with its train! Shivers chased up and down David's spine and his stomach seemed to be turning over. The little engine stood on the track puffing as if impatient to be off. It looked just like the picture—and, sure enough, there was David Matthews, the engineer! Next to the engine was the tender with wood for fuel, and behind that the coaches, bright yellow with orange trimmings. Some of the passengers chose to sit on top of the coaches, but the aunts were sure it would be safer inside. Besides they remembered about the sparks. Now they were all settled. The conductor came to collect the tickets.

"All aboard!" The conductor climbed on a small seat behind the tender and blew a long blast on a tin horn. "All aboard!"

"Can't we get out even now?" asked Aunt Ann, nervously clasping and unclasping her mittened hands.

"Nonsense, Ann," said Aunt Melissa. "We must do it for David's sake." Her voice was firm, but her knees were trembling.

S-s-s-s-ssss! a great sound of steam.

S-s-s-s-s-sss! Chuff! They were off!

It was jerky, but not nearly as bad as Sally Jones had said it was. Undoubtedly there had been changes and improvements. How quickly they traveled! The coaches rocked and swayed. The engine puffed out great clouds of black smoke. The aunts sat bolt upright, hands clasped tightly on their laps, looking perfectly miserable. David looked perfectly happy. He talked all the time.

"We're out in the country now! Oh, look at those cows, they're scared of us!"

"Look at those children on the fence. They're so surprised to see me riding on the train!"

"O-oh! We scared a horse! See him go down the road!"

"Ouch! There's a spark on me. It's all right, I put it out."

"The cows are scared of us!"

"Your cheek is all black, Aunt Melissa. No, not that one, the other one."

"There's another horse that's scared! I wonder what he thinks we are."

After a time David did not talk so much and the aunts did not sit so stiffly. They were getting quite accustomed to riding on the train. Aunt Ann began to look out of the windows with a good deal of pleasure.

"After all . . . Melissa . . ."

"After all you *like* it, don't you, Aunt Ann?" asked David.

Aunt Ann swallowed hard and looked the other way. Aunt Melissa answered.

"Why, yes, David, it seems almost pleasant. We shall undoubtedly use the train a number of other times."

David leaned back in his seat with a deep sigh of happiness.

"I shall go with you every time," he said. "And when I grow up I shall drive an engine just like David Matthews. Won't that be fine, Aunt Melissa?"

But Aunt Melissa had no time to answer for they were at the end of the line.

"Schenectady! Schenectady! All out!"

The journey on the small yellow train was over.

THE KITTEN ON THE CANAL BOAT

WHICH IS THE STORY OF HARRIET
WHO LIVED ON A CANAL BOAT

THIS HAPPENED IN OHIO
IN THE YEAR 1840

THE KITTEN ON THE CANAL BOAT

HARRIET lay in her narrow bunk watching pictures move slowly past, framed in the small, square window. Each morning the pictures were different: sometimes a patch of blue sky, white clouds, or green fields, sometimes sheep grazing or cows lying lazily under a tree. Harriet was quite accustomed to moving scenery, for all of her nine summers had been spent on a canal boat. In the winter months Harriet lived in a house, but she much preferred the time spent on the canal where something interesting and different was always happening.

Now the sun was coming in the small, square window and it was time to get up. Harriet jumped out of bed and climbed on a box to look out. The *Red Lion of the West* was nosing slowly along the canal and there was nothing to be seen but fields full of buttercups. Harriet was glad that it was a fine day, for it meant that as the *Red*

Lion passed through the next town gay picnic parties might come on board.

Two kinds of people traveled on the sturdy slow-moving canal boats. There were serious people who were really going somewhere. These slept on the boat and either brought their food with them or had their meals cooked by Harriet's mother in the tiny kitchen. These travelers sometimes were moving from one town or village to another, so they brought with them many bundles and baskets, with a large part of their household belongings. Then there were the gay people who were not really going anywhere but who thought it fun to take a trip on the boat. Harriet loved these picnic parties with laughing ladies who held little parasols over their heads to keep the sun from spoiling their beautiful complexions. They always carried the most interesting lunches put up in dainty baskets.

When Harriet was dressed she went to the kitchen. It was a neat little kitchen with red-checked curtains and a red geranium in the window. These matched the rest of the *Red Lion* which was a trim boat painted red and white with a black stripe. As Harriet entered the kitchen a good smell of crisp bacon came from the frying pan on the small stove. There were other important things to be done, however, so she did not waste much time over breakfast. From a basket in the corner she took two kittens, a gray one and a black one. With a kitten tucked under each arm she went out on the roof of the boat, which was quite flat, like a deck. There she stood and watched her brother, who was walking along the towpath beside Jerry and Jim, the mules that pulled the boat. At the stern stood Harriet's father with his hand on the tiller; it was his job to steer the boat.

Harriet put the kittens down on the deck and sat looking along the canal. This was an exciting day, for on this day the *Red Lion* passed the *Blossoming Bough*, the boat on which lived Harriet's friend, Alice. As the boats passed each other Harriet and Alice waved, and even had time to talk. Now, as Harriet watched, the *Blossoming Bough* turned the corner and came slowly down the canal. She was a pretty boat, as trim as the *Red Lion* but painted green and white with a touch of yellow. As the boats came near each other the *Blossoming Bough* drew off to one side to allow the *Red Lion* to pass. The tow lines were dropped so that the mules pulling the *Red Lion* could step over them.

Harriet stood as close to the edge of the deck as she dared. There was Alice close to the edge of *her* boat. It was well to be careful, for the deck had no railing and canal water was dark and cold.

"Harriet!" called Alice, "I have a new dress."

"What is it like?" asked Harriet.

"Oh, it's white, for Sundays. I'm not allowed to wear it on week days."

"I'm going to have a new dress soon," said Harriet.

"A Sunday dress?"

"Yes, I think it will be white like yours."

The *Red Lion* had slipped past the *Blossoming Bough*.

"Good-by, Harriet!"

"Good-by, Alice!"

There would be no more excitement now until the *Red Lion of the West* reached the next town. Harriet sat on the deck and played with the kittens. Suddenly her father put a horn to his lips and blew a long blast. Harriet ducked her head, for this meant that they were about to pass under a low bridge. It seemed no time at all until they reached the town—and there was a picnic party! It was a particularly interesting picnic party.

There were two pretty ladies with parasols, and two gentlemen, their hats tied to their buttonholes with string to keep them from blowing away. And there was a little girl. Harriet thought, as the little girl stepped daintily onto the deck, that she had never seen anything so beautiful or so exactly like a picture come to life. The little girl had blue eyes, yellow curls, and pink cheeks. Her dress was of the palest pink, and below it showed white lace-trimmed pantalettes. Harriet stood there feeling very dark and solid and different in her calico dress. She could not take her eyes off the little girl. There above the golden curls was a bonnet, a dainty straw bonnet trimmed with pink roses and tied under its owner's chin with a pink bow.

The ladies moved gracefully to a seat, arranged their skirts and sat chatting with the gentlemen. The little girl's mother called her to sit beside her. For five minutes the little girl sat there as prim and as quiet as a china ornament on a shelf. Then she saw the kittens.

"Oh, Mamma!" she said, "look at the darling kittens! A black one and a gray one. The gray one is just the kitten I want!"

"They belong to the little girl who lives on the boat," said her mother.

"Oh, but I *want* one," said the pink child, who had always had what she wanted. "I *want* one, Mamma, I want the gray one. It's my birthday, you know." Two large tears came into the blue eyes.

"Mercy, Florence," said her mother, looking worried, "don't cry! Let's ask the little girl if she will sell us the gray kitten."

"Little girl," said Florence, "will you sell us the gray kitten?"

"No!" said Harriet, her brown eyes very large, her feet planted firmly on the deck.

"But I *want* her," fretted the child.

"He's my favorite kitten," said Harriet.

"She's my favorite *kind* of kitten," said Florence even more fretfully. Then, as suddenly as the sun comes out from behind a cloud, she changed her tone and began to coax. "Won't you let me have her? Please?"

"Well," said Harriet, weakening, "perhaps I will. But *you* must give *me* something that I want very much."

"Oh, I *will!*" smiled Florence. "What is it?"

"Your lovely pink bonnet," answered Harriet.

There was a moment of chatter and fluttering.

"My pink bonnet?"

"Your lovely pink bonnet!"

"Your *new* pink bonnet. Florence, you *can't.*"

But Florence usually had her own way and this was her birthday. Once more two big tears came into her eyes. This time they fell and splashed on the pink dress. Slowly one hand began to untie the strings of the pink bonnet.

"No, Florence."

"Oh, please, Mamma."

"The sun is much too hot."

"Mamma, it's such a lovely day and I can share your parasol." By this time the bonnet was untied. Harriet picked up the gray kitten. With one hand she took the bonnet, with the other she gave up the gray kitten. Then she hurried into the kitchen to find her mother.

Mother shook her head over the queer ways of little girls, but at last she was persuaded that the exchange was a fair one. It was well that she thought so, for by this time wild horses could not have dragged the kitten from Florence's arms.

When the picnic was over a little girl without a bonnet stood on the shore and waved to another little girl on the deck of the canal boat.

"I'll be very kind to your nice gray kitten," called Florence. "And I'm going to call her Velvet."

"*His* name is Tom!" shouted Harriet, but the *Red Lion* was too far along the canal for the pink child to hear. This was just as well, for never in the world could she have owned a kitten with the plain name of Tom.

It was Sunday morning when next the *Red Lion of the West* passed the *Blossoming Bough*. The sound of church bells came faintly across the fields. It was very quiet on the canal. The boats slipped silently along, for on Sundays they were not allowed to blow their horns. Harriet stood as close to the edge of the deck as she dared. Alice stood close to the edge, too. Each little girl was wearing a Sunday dress. Each dress was white, with white pantalettes. Alice's hair was blowing in the breeze, but on Harriet's head there was a bonnet, a dainty straw bonnet with pink roses and pink ribbons tied under the chin.

"Look at my Sunday dress!" screamed Alice.

"Look at mine!"

"Why, Harriet, you have a pink bonnet!"

"Yes, isn't it beautiful?"

There was quite a long silence while Alice took in all the glory of the pink bonnet.

"It's the most beautiful bonnet I ever saw."

Harriet turned around to show the back of the bonnet.

"Did your mother give it to you?"

"His name is Tom!" shouted Harriet.

"No, I got it from a little girl in exchange for a kitten."

"For *what?*" The boats had passed each other.

"*For a kitten!*"

But the *Red Lion of the West* was now too far away from the *Blossoming Bough.* There was nothing to do but wait until they passed again, then Harriet and Alice could finish their conversation. It was often like that!

THE HOME ON WHEELS

WHICH IS THE STORY OF HOW
RICHARD AND ELLEN TRAVELED
WEST IN A COVERED WAGON

THIS HAPPENED IN THE YEAR 1852

THE HOME ON WHEELS

RICHARD and Ellen could not sleep that first night in the covered wagon. Mother and baby Hugh were fast asleep; one could hear their deep, even breathing. To the two older children it was all so thrilling that they could not settle down. Through the canvas flaps of the wagon they could see the dark sky, studded with stars. Some of the men were still talking by the camp fire. Richard sighed and pulled the blanket closer. It was warm and comfortable in the wagon but he would like to be outside. For a long time the children lay there drowsily, then somehow they fell asleep.

In the morning all kinds of noises awakened them, the bustle of people getting ready to start, loud talk of the trail and of the gold that lay at the end of it, high spirits for the first exciting days of the journey. There was not much room to dress in the wagon, for there was so much of everything in it. Barrels of flour with eggs neatly packed in the middle, other food supplies, tools, clothing, bedding, even the clock that mother prized so highly and would not leave behind. The first breakfast in the open air! The morning was crisp and cool and the bacon sizzled cheerfully. Why did people talk of the hardships of the overland trail?

That night the travelers sat around the campfire. Luke played on his fiddle. Philip played on his flute. The thin, sad little tune trickled out into the darkness.

> "Home, home, sweet, sweet home,
> Be it ever so humble there's no place like home!"

There was a choking sound from one of the women. She was thinking of the comfortable home she had left in Iowa. Nothing but a home on wheels for months to come!

"Play something cheery, Luke!" whispered one of the men. Luke drew the bow across the strings of his fiddle and swung into a rousing tune.

> "Oh, Susannah,
> Don't you cry for me,
> For I'm going to California
> With my wash bowl on my knee."

Voices joined in. The fire crackled and the darkness was full of song. Richard and Ellen were sorry when it was time for bed.

Those first days were not unpleasant in spite of bad roads. In the daytime there was a long trail of white-topped wagons with men and cows walking beside them. At night the wagons formed a corral or closed circle for protection in case of an Indian attack. Much to the relief of the older people, but rather to the disappointment of the children, they saw few Indians. One morning as they were breaking camp a small group of Indians did ride up, but they seemed to be merely curious and inclined to be friendly. Richard was standing by the wagon with Hugh in his arms. The morning sun shone on the baby's red-gold curls and one of the Indians gave a grunt of approval. He got down from his horse, pointed to the baby, to himself and then to the horse. He would trade the horse for the baby! Richard held Hugh tightly, shook his head, and stepped back into the shelter of the wagon. When the Indians rode away Richard gave a sigh of relief.

There was often the excitement and danger of crossing rivers. The first river was deep and muddy and there were only two flat boats to ferry hundreds of wagons across. That meant a long wait. Some streams were shallow and could be forded by the wagons. The oxen were urged in and soon the water came up to the tops of the wheels. It was a queer experience to sit in the wagon and watch the water swirling almost at one's feet. If only the stream did not get too deep! The worst crossing was a deep river where there were no ferries. There the men had to take the wagon bodies off the wheels and caulk the seams with tar so that the flat bodies could be used as boats. All the goods and supplies had to be unpacked, taken across the river and packed again.

On and on went the wagons, over roads so thick with dust that one could not see ahead. At night Richard and Ellen slept warmly in the wagon, Ellen wrapped in a blue and white coverlet which her grandmother had woven. Down in the corner of it was her grandmother's name and the date. The coverlet was Ellen's favorite possession and it was going all the way to California. It would make her feel more settled to see its familiar blue and white pattern on the bed in a new home.

On and on! Over roads even worse than before plodded the wagons, over mountains, through valleys, and over barren plains. On and on and on! They came to the grassy meadows before a long desert. Everyone had to turn to and make hay to feed the oxen during the days when there would be no grass. Then the hardest part of the journey was begun. The ground was hard and crusted with alkali. The sun was burning hot. Everyone who could walk beside the wagons did so to spare the oxen. Ellen rode with baby Hugh, Father and Mother and Richard walked. On and on! Now the sand was heavy and deep, the wheels of the wagons sank in it. Deserted wagons and dead oxen told the tale of difficulties met by other emigrants.

"We'll never make it," said the men. "The loads must be lightened."

All the heavy things went first, cook stoves and barrels of supplies. Still the wagon wheels moved heavily and the oxen strained at their yokes. The poor animals were growing tired. If they died there would be no hope of getting out of the desert. Men, women and children looked worn and anxious.

The day came when everything that could be taken out to lighten the wagons was taken out. Richard and Ellen helped to carry the things to the side of the trail and pile them up. All their cherished belongings, with Mother's clock ticking steadily on top of the pile.

"Oh, Father," said Ellen, "must I leave Grandmother's coverlet? *Please* let me keep it."

"We'll have to leave it," said Father grimly. "It's leave everything now, or die ourselves."

They were near the edge of the desert now.

The blue coverlet joined the pathetic pile at the side of the trail, so did Richard's gray blanket. The men made a sign such as they had seen in other places, "Help yourself." Perhaps a lighter wagon would be able to use some of the things they had discarded.

"I hope someone will take my blue coverlet," said Ellen sadly.

"Most likely before the week is out an Indian baby will be wrapped in it," said Richard.

"Don't tease your sister, Richard," said Mother fretfully. "We have troubles enough without that."

They were near the edge of the desert now and it was well, for the water casks were almost empty. A different danger lay ahead, for in the distance were the snow-capped peaks of a great range of mountains. Ellen felt weak and tired. As she lay in her bed at night an endless procession of dreary scenes went through her mind. Burning hot days on the prairies; choking dust; sand, miles and miles of it; the kitchen clock and the blue coverlet by the side of the trail; Bright, their favorite ox, lying dead; heat; thirst, baby Hugh crying pitifully for water; hunger. Now she was sure that she knew all the hardships of the California trail.

Mountain travel was dangerous, but a welcome change. These mountains were worse than those that they had passed. There were times when wagons had to be unpacked and lowered over precipices, or dragged up a steep rocky wall. At other times they toiled up long hills almost too steep for the oxen, or went through deep, gloomy ravines. It was solemn and lonely in the mountains and nights were cold. Everyone longed for the warm coverings left behind in the desert.

At last the road began to go downward. The grass was fresh and green and full of flowers. California was near! The travelers were at the end of the trail, and there was a pleasant grassy valley and a good place to camp. That night there was music and cheery talk around the camp fire. Richard and Ellen listened to a surprising conversation between two of the older men. One of them said solemnly, "Providence has blessed and favored us through this long journey." "Indeed," said the other, "we have avoided accident and disease and have traveled smoothly and quietly." Richard and Ellen gave each other a wondering look. Evidently the journey had been an easy one!

The story might end here with the making of new homes. For Ellen it ended later, when in the cabin of one of the settlers she saw a blue and white coverlet on a bed. Ellen lifted a corner of it and looked. There was the woven name:

ELLEN ADAIR

Her grandmother's name! Ellen dropped the corner of the coverlet without saying a word. The sign had said, "Help yourself"; she had no right to the coverlet now. That was just a part of life on the trail.

NEW SHOES FOR DIAMOND

WHICH IS THE STORY OF HOW EDWIN SAW A BALLOON ASCENSION IN NEW YORK

NEW SHOES FOR DIAMOND

CLING, clang, cling! The blacksmith brought his hammer down on the red-hot horseshoe. Edwin stepped back a little as the sparks flew near him. Now the shoe was ready—a sizzling plunge in water and the glowing heat died out. The blacksmith's assistant finished paring Diamond's hoof, and the new shoe was nailed into place. Diamond had two new shoes. Prince, who was standing in a stall at one side of the shop had not needed to be shod.

It was cool in the blacksmith's shop, if one did not stand *too* close to the fire, dark and cool. Outside, the hot summer sun shone through the trees and made patterns of bright gold on the street. Edwin wished he could spend the whole day in the shop and explore all the dark corners. It was an enchanting place with its queer little glass windows, some of the panes cracked and covered with spider webs. A straight ladder led up to a loft which Edwin was sure must be full of the most interesting things. Why must he go home?

There was no time to linger, however, for James was leading Diamond toward the carriage that stood waiting outside. The blacksmith's helper was leading Prince. Edwin hurried over to the forge.

"Please," he said to the blacksmith, "please may I have a horseshoe to take home?"

"Take your pick," laughed the blacksmith. "They do say a horseshoe brings luck."

On the floor was a great pile of horseshoes of every size. Edwin considered a very small one that must have belonged to a pony. Then he found an enormous shoe that could only have fitted a large cart horse. He threw both of these aside, however, and chose one of Diamond's old shoes.

"Edwin!" called James. "Where are you?"

Edwin ran out into the sunlight. The horses were harnessed and waiting. Diamond was pawing the ground as if he could scarcely wait to try his new shoes. Edwin climbed to the high box seat beside James. He had not ridden there before to-day. Things looked very different up there, one could even see right over the tops of garden walls.

"It's a good thing Diamond has new shoes," said Edwin. "We are going to the park this afternoon."

"A very good thing," agreed James.

"I think shoeing a horse is the most interesting thing in the world," said Edwin.

"Well," said James, "that's a matter of opinion. Last week I saw a man go up in a big fire balloon. All decorated the balloon was, with ribbons, and it was a fine sight. Flying through the air, that's what *I* call the most interesting thing in the world."

"I wish Papa would take me to see a balloon go up," sighed Edwin. "Maybe if I hang Diamond's shoe up in my room it will bring me luck. Then some day Papa will say, 'Edwin, do you want to go to see a balloon ascension?' "

James turned to look at the horseshoe.

"Your mama won't like that, Edwin," he grinned.

"I know she won't," said Edwin. "But she'll let me keep it in my own room."

They were home now. James reined up the horses in front of a tall brownstone house, with a steep flight of steps leading up to a very solemn-looking front door. Edwin climbed down from the box and ran up the steps. A maid opened the door and let him in.

"Hurry, Edwin. Your papa and mama are waiting for you and they are getting out of patience."

Edwin hurried in the front door. It was so dark after the sunlit street that he found it hard to pick his way among the many little tables laden with china ornaments. Mama was seated in one of the green and gold chairs. Lucy, Edwin's sister, sat on a low footstool. Papa was pacing up and down the room. There was no doubt that he was impatient.

"Edwin!" Papa's voice sounded very loud in the quiet room. "Why have you been so long?"

"I'm sorry, Papa," answered Edwin, "but Diamond had to have *two* new shoes."

"Edwin," said Mama in her quiet, ladylike voice, "why are you carrying that dirty old horseshoe?"

"For luck," answered Edwin. "I'll keep it in my room."

"Well, put it down now, and let us get started," said Papa. "If we don't hurry we'll miss the balloon ascension."

"The *what?*" asked Edwin, feeling sure he was dreaming.

"The balloon ascension. Don't you want to see it?"

Words failed Edwin. He nodded his head. Never could he have dreamed that luck would come so quickly! He put the horseshoe down on the hall floor with a clatter. Then the family went out to the waiting carriage.

Up Fifth Avenue they went, past fine houses with beautiful gardens. Edwin was not interested in anything, not even in the big reservoir at Forty-second Street, though usually he had many questions to ask about that. It seemed a long time until they reached the place where the balloon was to go up. Crowds were gathered. Carriages with fine high-stepping horses drove up. No horses, however, stepped more proudly or held their heads higher than Prince and Diamond.

The balloon, a great round thing filled with hot air, was tugging at its ropes. As the men who were holding the ropes released them the balloon rose and floated over the heads of the crowd. A trapeze hung below it, on which, as the balloon rose higher and higher, an acrobat turned and twisted and somersaulted. When the balloon was quite high, the acrobat jumped, his parachute opened, and he floated slowly down. The crowd gasped.

There was dead silence for a minute. "They've done it!" someone shouted.

Then the crowd broke loose. "Hurrah! Hurrah! Hurrah!"

The shouts frightened the horses. James had all he could do to hold Prince and Diamond. They tossed their heads and pranced nervously.

Higher and higher sailed the balloon. The crowd grew calmer. Carriages began to drive away.

"Hurrah! Hurrah! They're off!"

"Oh—let's stay a little longer," begged Edwin.

The balloon looked very small against a blue sky. It drifted over toward the river.

"I hope it doesn't come down in the water," said Lucy.

"It's all very dangerous," said Mama. "Why can't people be content to stay on the ground? Man was never meant to fly in the air."

"Nonsense!" said Papa. "One of these days, man will fly as easily as he walks."

Mama frowned and shook her head. "Don't fill the children's heads with such ideas!"

The carriage turned south on Fifth Avenue. Edwin settled back in his seat with a little sigh of happiness. Down the avenue they went, Diamond stepping proudly in his new shoes. Now they were back at the tall brownstone house. Mama and Papa and Lucy went up the steep steps. Edwin waited a moment to pat Diamond on his velvety nose.

"Diamond," he said, "yours must be the luckiest shoes in all New York. To-morrow you shall have a lump of sugar."

MARY JANE AND THE BUGGY

WHICH IS THE STORY OF HOW
MARY JANE AND ROGER DROVE
THE OLD WHITE HORSE

THIS HAPPENED IN THE YEAR 1890

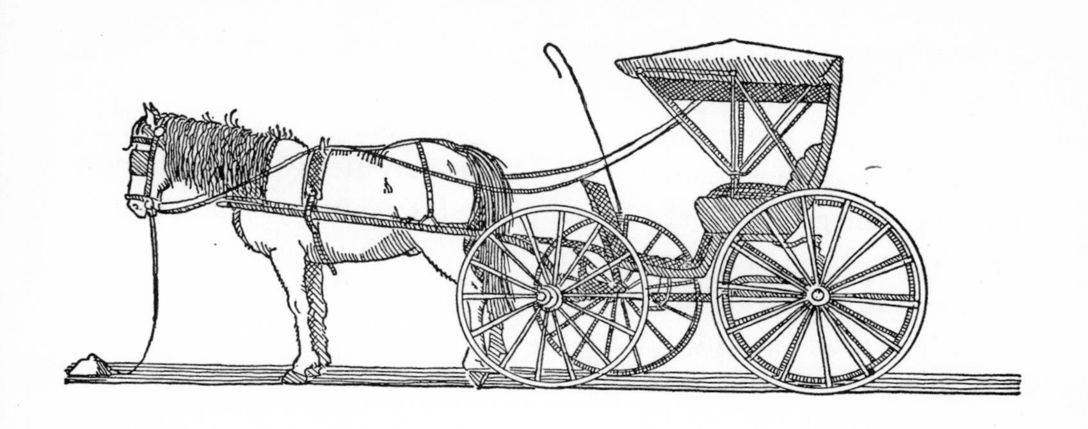

MARY JANE AND THE BUGGY

MARY JANE and Roger were the children of a country doctor. Sometimes when the doctor went on his rounds he took the children with him. They loved to drive along the country roads in the buggy behind Dan, the old white horse. Mary Jane began by holding the ends of the reins and pretending that she was driving. Then she really learned to drive. Roger was too young for this, so to make up for it the doctor let him hold the whip. Occasionally Roger gave Dan the tiniest flick with the whip, but it had to be a very tiny one, for Dan was used to kind treatment.

One day the doctor was away at a meeting in a near-by town.

"Mary Jane," said her mother, "I wish you would take this jelly over to old Mrs. Harris. Your father always forgets to take it."

"Mother," said Mary Jane, "it's so hot and that's such a long walk. May I take the buggy?"

"All by yourself?" asked her mother. "You have never driven it alone."

"I *can*," said Mary Jane. "I'm nine years old."

"Well," said her mother, "old Dan is very steady and I suppose you can manage him. Take Roger along for company. And remember, Mary Jane, that unless you drive carefully going downhill Dan will sit down, and then where will you be?"

"I'll be most careful," promised Mary Jane.

Half an hour later the buggy started on its way with Mary Jane proudly holding the reins and Roger holding the whip.

"Don't you touch Dan with the whip!" called his mother. She stood and watched the buggy until it was out of sight.

"I wonder if I should have let them go," she said as she went into the house. "Old Dan is pretty reliable unless he meets a steam roller. I hope there isn't one of *those* around."

It was a beautiful sunny day. The sky was blue and the fields were full of flowers. Mary Jane thought it would be nice to stop and pick some daisies. Old Mrs. Harris would like some and so would Mother. She drew up at the side of the road, and twisted the reins around a fence post. Then she and Roger went into the field. There were daisies and buttercups and black-eyed Susans. It took quite a long time to pick a large bunch. The flies bothered Dan and he tossed his head and stamped impatiently.

"Dan doesn't like waiting," said Roger. "We must go on, Mary Jane."

"I suppose we must," said Mary Jane.

They climbed into the buggy and started off once more.

Soon they came to a tiny house in front of which played a two-year-old baby.

"Oh," said Mary Jane, "Father told me that there was a new baby at this house only two weeks ago. We must stop and see it. I do like little new, pink babies." So they stopped Dan by the gate and went in to see the baby. It was very new and very pink as it lay in its cradle. Mary Jane loved the way its tiny fingers curled around hers.

"Let's go on," said Roger, who was not especially fond of new pink babies.

They drove on. At the gate of a low brown house they stopped because a pleasant woman waved to them.

"Well, Mary Jane and Roger!" said the woman. "Wherever are you going?"

"We are taking some jelly to old Mrs. Harris," said Mary Jane importantly.

"Oh, indeed! Then perhaps you haven't time to come in and taste my nice warm gingerbread? I've just taken it out of the oven."

Mary Jane sniffed. Roger sniffed. There was a perfectly lovely smell of warm gingerbread in the air. There was nothing to do but stop, and in a few minutes they were in Mrs. Brown's kitchen drinking milk and eating some of her fresh golden-brown gingerbread. A whinny from Dan reminded them that they should be on their way.

Along the road they went with only a few stops to look at the Smiths' new baby chickens and Aunt Ella's garden. At last they came to the long hill that was just before Mrs. Harris' house.

"Aren't we having a nice time?" said Mary Jane dreamily. "Daisies and gingerbread and babies—" She slackened her hold on the reins. If there was one thing old Dan hated it was to feel the weight of the buggy hurrying him down a hill. Before the children knew it he braced himself against the dashboard and sank gracefully to his haunches.

"Roger!" gasped Mary Jane. "Dan is sitting down."

"I knew it!" said Roger. "What are you going to do, Mary Jane?"

"I don't know," said Mary Jane sadly. "There isn't anyone on the road to help us." They climbed out of the buggy once more and stood looking sadly at Dan who stared unblinkingly ahead with his mild brown eyes.

"Oh, Dan," said Mary Jane, "why did you have to do it? Can't you get up? We'll never get home and Mother will be so worried."

Old Dan sat there steadily, with only a flick of his ear as a fly settled on it. As a matter of fact he could not get up without assistance.

What was to be done? The children sat on the grassy bank and stared gloomily at Dan. It seemed hours, though it was really only a short time, before they heard the welcome sound of wheels and two men came along in a wagon. The men laughed when they saw Dan, but they stopped the wagon, unharnessed the horse and pushed and urged him to his feet.

"Now we must hurry," said Mary Jane as old Dan started briskly on once more.

The jelly was left at Mrs. Harris' and Dan trotted briskly homeward. There were no stops on the way.

At their own gate the children saw their mother waiting. "Mercy's sakes, where *have* you been?" she called. "I've been worrying about you for an hour."

Mary Jane pulled Dan up with a flourish. Roger put the whip back in the socket. Together, in a somewhat jumbled way, they ex-

"Dan is sitting down!"

plained about daisies and gingerbread and babies and old Dan's sitting down on the hill. Their mother laughed but she also shook her head.

"Children, children," she said, "I might have known! Next time I want an errand done it will be quicker for you to walk!"

"But we did have such fun," said Mary Jane, "and we have brought you a perfectly beautiful bunch of daisies!"

HARVEY AND HIGGINS INCORPORATED

WHICH IS THE STORY OF TWO BOYS
AND THE FIRST AUTOMOBILE THAT
CAME TO THEIR TOWN

THIS HAPPENED IN THE MIDDLE WEST
IN THE YEAR 1902

HARVEY AND HIGGINS INCORPORATED

JIM HARVEY and Dan Higgins lived in a small town in the middle west. It was a nice town on the edge of a lake, with pleasant houses and tree-bordered streets. Jim and Dan lived next door to each other; they were eight and nine years old and great friends. Jim had red hair and freckles and he was short and fat. Dan had brown curly hair and blue eyes and he was tall and thin. However, although the two boys looked so different they really were quite alike in their ways and liked many of the same things.

One of the things that was the same about Jim and Dan was their birthday. It came on the same day, which was the thirtieth of July, right in the middle of the summer vacation. On the day that Jim was eight and Dan nine Jim woke up early. There were no presents by his bed. At the breakfast table there were no presents and no one seemed even to know that it was his birthday. After breakfast he went out in the yard and leaned over the fence to talk to Dan.

"Hullo, Dan!" said Jim.

"Hullo, Jim!" said Dan.

"I didn't get any presents for my birthday."

"I didn't either."

"Do you suppose they *forgot?*"

At that moment Jim's father came out into the Harvey back yard and Dan's father came out into the Higgins yard.

"Jim," said Mr. Harvey, "come down to the barn. I have something to show you."

"Dan," said Mr. Higgins, "come down to the barn. I have something to show you."

The barn was dark when Jim went into it and he could not see very clearly. In one stall stood Bess, the mare his father drove in the buggy. In the other stall was a small dark shape. It moved. Jim's eyes were beginning to be accustomed to the darkness and he could see that it was a pony, a very small dark-brown pony with a shaggy coat.

"What do you think of that for a birthday present?" asked his father.

"A birthday present! Dad! Is it really mine?"

His father nodded. "Take the halter and lead him out to show Danny."

Jim took the halter and led the little pony out very carefully. His heart was thumping so against his chest that he could scarcely breathe. Now he and the small brown pony were out in the sunny yard.

"Hi, Danny!" Jim's shout died off suddenly for there was Dan with a pony exactly like his own. Both fathers were watching them and laughing.

"You'll find saddles in the barn," said Mr. Harvey. "I guess you both know what to do with them."

They did. For a year the boys had wanted a pony more than anything in the world and they had practiced riding Tom Smith's pony. They had hoped only for one pony and now there were two. That day was "the best day we have had in all our lives," as Jim said to Dan. They rode the ponies and gave turns to all the children in the neighborhood.

For several weeks everything went well. Then Mr. Harvey and Mr. Higgins, who were business partners, lost a great deal of money.

"I'm afraid the ponies will have to go," said Mr. Harvey. "They cost a good deal to keep and I am selling Bessie."

"Oh, Dad, can't we keep them? Can't we keep them if Dan and I earn the money to feed them?"

"Well, perhaps, but how can you earn the money?"

"We'll think of a way."

So Jim and Dan thought and thought, but they could not think of a plan. At last an idea came to Danny.

"Jim, I know! Let's fix up our wagon and deliver things for the stores."

"Could we, would they let us?"

"They'll have to. Come on!"

The wagon in which the boys sometimes drove their ponies was fixed up. The boys painted it a very bright blue. On each side of it they painted in rather crooked letters:

HARVEY AND HIGGINS
INCORPORATED

"Partners are 'incorporated,' " said Jim who had seen the word on their fathers' office door.

"I don't know exactly what it means, but anyway it looks well on the wagon," said Dan.

So Harvey and Higgins were started in business, and it was surprising how the business grew. At first they delivered a few packages for the hardware store. Then they took flowers for the florist. Soon the smaller stores began to find out that people liked to have the blue wagon and the two small ponies trot up to their door and deliver a package. So the boys found that each day after school there were interesting packages to be taken to houses all over the town.

One afternoon Harvey and Higgins left the bakers with a most exciting package. There were other packages, too, but placed very carefully in the middle of the wagon was a large box done up in white paper and tied with an enormous silvery bow. It was Dorothea May Armstrong's birthday cake. Dorothea May lived in the largest house in town, a house to which Harvey and Higgins had always wanted to deliver a package.

"Do you suppose they'll ask us to take it in?" asked Jim as they drove carefully along Main Street. "I've always wanted to see inside that house."

"Maybe they will," said Danny. "Look, Jim! What's the crowd on the corner over by the hotel?"

"Let's drive over and see," said Jim.

Over by the hotel a crowd had gathered and was staring curiously at a large black object.

"It's one of those new horseless carriages!" said Dan excitedly. "We never saw one here before. Let's go nearer." So they drove nearer. The strange black carriage was making queer, purring sounds. It coughed, it snorted, it choked. The crowd laughed. The tall man who sat in it looked annoyed. He climbed out and turned a handle in the front of the machine, ran back, climbed in, turned something else, and the machine leaped forward with a mighty roar that scattered the crowd and made the babies burst into surprised howls.

And the ponies of Harvey and Higgins Incorporated! Never had they seen anything like the noisy black object! Like twin streaks of lightning off they went along Main Street with Harvey shouting, "Whoa!" and Higgins hanging on to the lines. Packages were scattered everywhere. When finally the ponies came to a standstill heaving and sweating and rolling their terrified eyes, Dan and Jim looked blankly at each other.

"The birthday cake!"

Sadly they went back along Main Street walking beside the ponies. Friendly onlookers handed them the packages, some decidedly the worse for wear. Close by the hotel a boy who was in Dan's class at school held the large silver-ribboned package in his arms.

"Hey, Danny! This slid off just as you started. I caught it!"

Dan and Jim heaved sighs of relief. "Maybe it isn't hurt." They untied the box carefully and peered into the package. A dozen or so boys and girls gathered around and peered too. There was the cake quite unharmed, glittering with its white frosting and pink flowers and silver trimmings. It was safe!

Then Dan happened to look up at the clock. Three forty-five, and the party was to be at four! The Armstrong house was at the other end of town. They couldn't make it. For the first time Harvey and Higgins would fail to deliver a package and so would be utterly disgraced.

"Well, boys! I'm sorry my automobile scared your ponies," said a voice. "I'll make it good with you about those packages."

They looked up to see the owner of the car that had made the trouble. He looked so friendly that in a minute they were telling him the whole sad tale of the birthday cake.

"Can't deliver it, you say? Why not? There's my machine right around the corner, it'll get us there in two shakes of a lamb's tail. Get a boy to drive your ponies home and off we'll go. You'll be the first boys in this town to ride in an automobile!"

The first boys in the town to ride in an automobile! Harvey and Higgins could scarcely believe it was not a dream. There they were, rattling along Main Street, Danny holding the box with the cake very carefully on his knees. People stood still on the sidewalks to look at them. Jim hoped that none of the boys in his class would miss the sight. The first boys in the town to ride in a horseless carriage! He wondered if it were very dangerous, but he did not much care if it were.

There was a bang and a clatter. The machine stopped short and no amount of coaxing would make it go. The gentleman got out, lifted the hood in front and peered inside. Then he came back, got a tool and fussed with the machinery. It seemed a long time before the car was ready to start.

"I think we could have got there quicker with our ponies!" whispered Jim to Dan.

A crowd of small boys gathered to watch what was going on. They snickered and giggled.

No amount of coaxing would make it go.

"Get a horse!" suggested one of the boys. Then they all joined in chanting loudly in chorus:

"Get a horse, Mister! Get a horse!"

Suddenly when the car was cranked something inside it began to purr softly. With a cough and a snort they were off again!

In no time at all they were puffing and snorting up the driveway of the Armstrong home. The butler came out of the house, his eyes almost popping out of his head. Dorothea May came running out too.

"Oh, Daddy! Mother! Bob! Susan!" she called. "Here's one of those queer new carriages."

The whole Armstrong family came out and stood on the doorstep. Danny climbed out of the car with a great deal of dignity and handed the large box to Dorothea May. "Your birthday cake!" he said. "A little late, I'm afraid, but it might never have got here at all." Then he climbed into the car again and off they puffed and snorted down the drive.

"I'm glad the ponies ran away!" whispered Jim to Dan. "If they hadn't run away we wouldn't have been the first boys in this town to ride in this machine."

Now Jim and Dan are grown up and in that very same town there is a handsome dark-blue delivery truck with HARVEY AND HIGGINS INCORPORATED painted on it in the neatest letters. Harvey and Higgins don't drive the truck themselves, though sometimes they look out of their office windows and wish that they did. It was such fun in the old days when they drove down Main Street in the blue wagon behind the two little brown ponies!

THE PICTURE STORY OF TRAVEL IN AMERICA DURING THE LAST HUNDRED YEARS

THIS PART OF THE BOOK IS FOR THOSE CHILDREN WHO WANT TO KNOW MORE ABOUT WAYS OF TRAVELING THAN IS TOLD IN THE STORIES

A HUNDRED years ago there were no photographs of stagecoaches, trains and boats. We know how they looked because artists painted them, sometimes on signs, and engraved them for newspapers, and for advertising posters. The artist who made the pictures for this book has used these old ones to help her with her drawings.

The Concord coach.

WHEELS AND HORSES

A COUNTRY without roads! Nothing but Indian trails through the forest! It took real courage for the first settlers in this country to travel from one place to another. The only way to travel any distance was on horseback; wheels could be used only after roads were made. A hundred years ago the chief method of travel was by coach. Large public coaches were known as "stages" because they changed horses at regular "stages" or divisions of the journey. The early stagecoaches had hard wooden seats and no springs so we can scarcely imagine how the travelers must have felt at the end of a trip over a rough road. Yet people thought this was a fine way to travel, spoke of a week's journey from Boston to New York as "expeditious" and called some of the stages "flying machines." Later there were fine coaches with their bodies hung on leather straps, which made riding somewhat more comfortable. There were exciting races between coaches, and those racing each other changed horses in a very few minutes and were off again. Stagecoaches were still in use fifty years ago. Long after there were trains some people preferred to travel by coach; this is not hard to understand, for there were many accidents on early railroads.

In towns and cities coaches soon became horse-drawn omnibuses. Some of these were very handsome, painted in bright colors with gold trimmings. Inside there might be paintings on the walls and small candles to give light. Nowadays if we want to go from the shopping district of New York to Greenwich Village, a Fifth Avenue bus will take us there in a fairly short time. But a hundred years ago Greenwich Village was a real country village and to travel there by stage from New York was quite a trip. The pictures show an omnibus on Broadway in New York, as well as some of the other horse-drawn vehicles of that time.

Goods as well as people had to move from one place to another, so large wagons drawn by four or six horses carried heavy loads. Some of these were called Conestoga wagons because they were first made at Conestoga Creek in Pennsylvania. Along the roads they went, one after another, blue wagons with red side boards and white canvas tops. The horses looked very gay, for their harness was decorated with bright-colored ribbons and scarlet fringe. Bells jangled

Horse-drawn street car.

on wooden arches over the horses' backs. The driver, with his long whip, walked beside the wagon or rode on a board at the side or on one of the horses. Years later these Conestoga wagons were used for the last time as the "prairie schooners" that took emigrants across the country on the long journey to the West.

It is interesting to remember that the first railroads were not built for locomotives but for cars drawn by horses. It was found that cars moved more easily on rails; they could go as fast as eight to fifteen miles an hour. Rails were made of wood with flat strips of iron fastened to them, and over these went the horse-drawn cars with a mighty roar. It was on the Baltimore and Ohio Railroad that a horse-drawn car raced a steam locomotive. One early railroad company advertised that on fine days the train would be pulled by a locomotive but on rainy days it would be drawn by horses!

For years street cars were drawn by horses. This was slow and in cold and icy weather it was hard on the animals. They sometimes slipped and fell down.

There was one way to travel by land without horses and that was on the velocipede or bicycle which, of course, was used only for short distances. The first velocipede was most amusing. It was nicknamed the "Dandy carriage" or "Hobbyhorse" and indeed it was not unlike a child's hobbyhorse. The rider moved the velocipede by pushing with his feet, which touched the ground! The next step was to get the feet off the ground, and an equally amusing bicycle with a huge front wheel and small back wheel was used. This was difficult to ride, so next the small wheel was placed in front. Then wheels became the same size and bicycles were much more useful and practical.

After a time people learned how to use steam, so horses were not quite so useful. They still drew buggies and carriages and wagons. In country places the doctor went his rounds in a buggy and people drove to church in buggies and gigs and surreys. Carriages were handsome affairs, with graceful bodies, and they were drawn by the finest of high-stepping horses. Only thirty years ago city parks were crowded with all kinds of horse-drawn conveyances. People who

The Hobbyhorse bicycle.

did not ride in carriages rode on bicycles. Then came automobiles, and the best days of horses were over.

Now horses are still used for riding. In a few country places they still draw buggies and wagons. In cities we see the fine horses of the mounted police. Autos and taxis and enormous buses roar past them, but the horses do not stir or look around. They are not like the horses that ran away when the early trains and automobiles came by. The horses of to-day have grown up in traffic. They are used to it.

Conestoga wagon.

Horse-drawn omnibus.

In the days of carriages and bicycles.

Packet boat.

THE DAYS OF SAIL

IN THE early days of sail, most ships on the Atlantic were square-rigged sailing ships. These ships were called packets because they carried mail, and in those days letters were large "packets" sealed with sealing wax. The packet boats were really the first "liners" for they sailed regularly from one port to another, supposedly in a straight line. They also sailed under the flag of one line or company. The ships of the famous Black Ball Line had a large black ball painted on one of the forward sails and flew a triangular flag with a black ball. The ships of the Red Cross Line had a red cross on flag and sail. The early packet boats were not very comfortable, especially for the steerage passengers. Sleeping quarters were crowded and dirty, food was very poor. Many of the ships were full of rats. The captain of a packet boat was scolded by his company because the letters that were carried on his ship were so nibbled by rats that the addresses could not be read! As time went on packet boats became more comfortable.

Clipper ship.

To shorten the time of voyages, and especially of the voyage to California, a different type of ship was built. These ships were long and slender, curving inward at the waterline, so that they could cut through the water more easily, and they had tall masts so that they could carry more sail. They were called "clipper" ships because they went through the water at such a fast clip. Clipper ships were first built in America, the most famous ones in the shipyards of Donald McKay, and the "Yankee clipper" was known everywhere for her speed and grace. The sea has never known anything more beautiful than a clipper ship under full sail. An old chantey shows the pride the sailors took in them:

> A Yankee ship comes down the river,
> Blow, boys, blow!
> Her masts and yards they shine like silver,
> Blow, my bully boys, blow!

What exciting races there were between the fast clipper ships! With favorable winds they could easily outsail the first steamboats. The clipper ship *Red Jacket* crossed the Atlantic in thirteen days and one hour, which was fast for a sailing ship.

After a time, however, sails gave way to steam. The tremendous sails of the ships were difficult to manage. It took courage on an icy winter night for men to climb almost to the top of a mast to struggle with a frozen, flapping sail. It was expensive, too, for a ship had to carry a large crew and sails were always having to be repaired. Nowadays a full-rigged ship is seldom seen on the ocean, even schooners are rare, and we have only pictures, ship models and ships at Mystic Seaport, Connecticut to remind us of the grand days of sail.

The John Fitch.

STEAM

IN THE year 1787 this country was just beginning to be interested in steam. The first steamboat that ever traveled on American water was made by John Fitch, and ran on the Delaware River. When the boat was launched at Philadelphia the governor of the state came to see the strange new invention and was so pleased with it that he gave John Fitch a beautiful silk flag. We can imagine the sailors on the big sailing ships of that time looking down with amusement as the small steamboat with its twelve side paddles puffed and snorted its way along. This boat and another improved model made many trips on the river, carrying passengers. Some people said, "John Fitch will make his fortune!" Others said, "Poor fellow, what a pity he is crazy!" John Fitch never *did* make his fortune. He made several steamboats, one of which was the first boat to have a screw propeller; this was tried out on Collect Pond in New York. People made so much fun of the inventor and his ideas that at last he was tired and discouraged and gave up trying to show how steam could be put to work.

The horse-drawn car, racing—

It was more than twenty years before people understood how useful steam could be. Then Robert Fulton built the *North River of Clermont*. When the *Clermont* made her first trip on the Hudson River crowds came to see her. They were sure that "Fulton's Folly," as they called the boat, would not move a foot from the dock. They were also sure that she would explode. As the little boat moved slowly away from the dock, her paddle wheels churning the water, her engines making a great noise, the crowd was too surprised to say anything at all. Then, as she began to move faster, and to go up the river *against* the wind, everyone cheered and shouted. The *Clermont* made the trip from New York to Albany in thirty hours at the rate of about five miles an hour. After that she made regular trips up and down the Hudson. Sparks and clouds of black smoke came from her tall smokestack and it was no wonder that people thought they were seeing some strange monster! The fishermen and boatmen on the river did not like the *Clermont* and they sometimes ran into her on purpose. Each time, however, she was repaired and went on her way up and down the river. Soon she was joined by a number of other steamboats.

It was one thing for a steamboat to travel on the calm water of a

—the Tom Thumb.

river and quite another thing for one to travel on water that was sometimes rough. So the first steamboat on the Great Lakes was also an experiment. This boat, which ran on Lake Erie from Buffalo to Detroit, was called *Walk-in-the-Water*. This, so the story goes, was the name given by the Indians to the first steamboats. No one used this long name, everyone said "The Steamboat."

After a few years' service "The Steamboat" was wrecked in a storm and another boat took her place.

One brave little steamboat tried a longer journey. The *Savannah* went all the way across the Atlantic. She was really a sailing vessel fitted with an engine and she was only one hundred and twenty feet long, less than one third the size of a small present-day liner. When the *Savannah* was ready to start, her owners advertised for passengers. Thirty-two fine cabins were waiting but not a single person could be found who was willing to risk the trip. So the *Savannah* sailed without either passengers or cargo. The supply of fuel was limited, and the captain did not think that paddles would be of much use in rough weather; so whenever the weather was rough the paddles were taken off and placed on deck. A sailing vessel saw

The Best Friend—

what seemed to be another ship on fire, so she hurried to the rescue. It was only the *Savannah* with her sails set and smoke coming from her funny little smokestack! After twenty-nine days, for eighty hours of which the *Savannah* had used steam, she made a proud entry into harbor with not a sail set. There was a great deal of excitement in England, and in the home port of Savannah when the steamboat returned. However, the *Savannah* was turned into a sailing vessel again, and for several years no other steamboat crossed the Atlantic. Then English boats made the crossing.

The first steamboats to cross the Atlantic regularly were those of the Cunard Line. There is an interesting story about one of these early Cunard boats. Some Englishmen who had come to visit the shipyards of Donald McKay wished to return in the shortest possible time. McKay offered them a passage on his fine ship, *Sovereign of the Seas*, but they were sure that a Cunard steamboat would be faster. The two boats started together but in mid-ocean the clipper passed the steamboat. When the steamboat's passengers landed in Liverpool they were surprised to see a large canvas sign which read:

—of Charleston.

SOVEREIGN OF THE SEAS
FASTEST SHIP IN THE WORLD
SAILED NEW YORK TO LIVERPOOL
RECORD TIME 13 DAYS 22 HOURS

It was not until steamboats were built of iron and steel and had screw propellers instead of side paddles that they took the place of the clipper ships. For a long time sailing ships were safer, for early steamboats were apt to catch fire or explode.

Meanwhile steam was also being used for railroad travel. A few years after John Fitch built his steamboats the city of Philadelphia was again surprised and disturbed. Such a queer thing had run through the streets! It ran without horses to pull it and it looked like a boat on wheels. It was a boat, a steam dredge. Oliver Evans, who made it, had only put it on wheels to show that steam might be used on land as well as on water. He said that trains worked by steam would soon travel from place to place at the remarkable speed of fifteen miles an hour. Nobody believed him.

The first really successful locomotive built in England was Ste-

The West Point—

phenson's *Rocket.* The first American-built locomotive to actually draw a passenger train was the *Tom Thumb.* This tiny engine was made by Peter Cooper and tried out on the Baltimore and Ohio Railroad, to prove that steam locomotives not only could pull cars but could go uphill and around curves. Although the engine was only a little over one horse power it made a speed of eighteen miles an hour during a part of its trial trip. The men who rode in the car were so excited that they took out their notebooks and wrote in them, just to show that this *could* be done when traveling at such a high speed. The owners of stage lines thought the locomotive would take away their trade, so they arranged for a race between a horse-drawn car and the steam train. How exciting that was! The passengers cheered wildly. Because of an accident the horse won the race, but the *Tom Thumb* had proved that cars *could* be pulled by steam, and the way was open for more experiments.

On Christmas Day, 1830, a great crowd assembled to see *The Best Friend of Charleston* make its first trip. A man who traveled on the train that day wrote an article for the local newspaper de-

—on its trial trip.

scribing the event and making a good deal of fun of it. He wrote, "We flew on the wings of the wind at the varied speed of fifteen to twenty miles an hour . . . 'leaving all the world behind.' " The engine, he said, went through the countryside "like a live rocket, scattering sparks and flames on every side." A year later there was a great celebration; the *Best Friend* had proved its worth, for a whole year it had pulled a train from Charleston to Hamburg. Cannons were fired, a band played, and everyone was gay and cheerful. Sad to say, a few months after that the *Best Friend* came to an untimely end. A Negro fireman did not care for the noise made by the steam escaping from the safety valve, so he closed the valve and sat on it. The boiler exploded, injuring a number of people and putting an end to the work of the little locomotive.

Shortly after the accident to the *Best Friend* another locomotive, the *West Point*, took its place. The *West Point* made another grand trial trip with many passengers and a Negro band on board. The passengers felt quite safe, for on a car behind the engine were piled bales of cotton to protect them in case of explosion. The *West Point* never did explode, which was fortunate for the passengers. After this came the *De Witt Clinton*, first locomotive to draw a passenger train in New York state. We can still see this little engine, in the Ford Museum, Greenfield Village, Michigan.

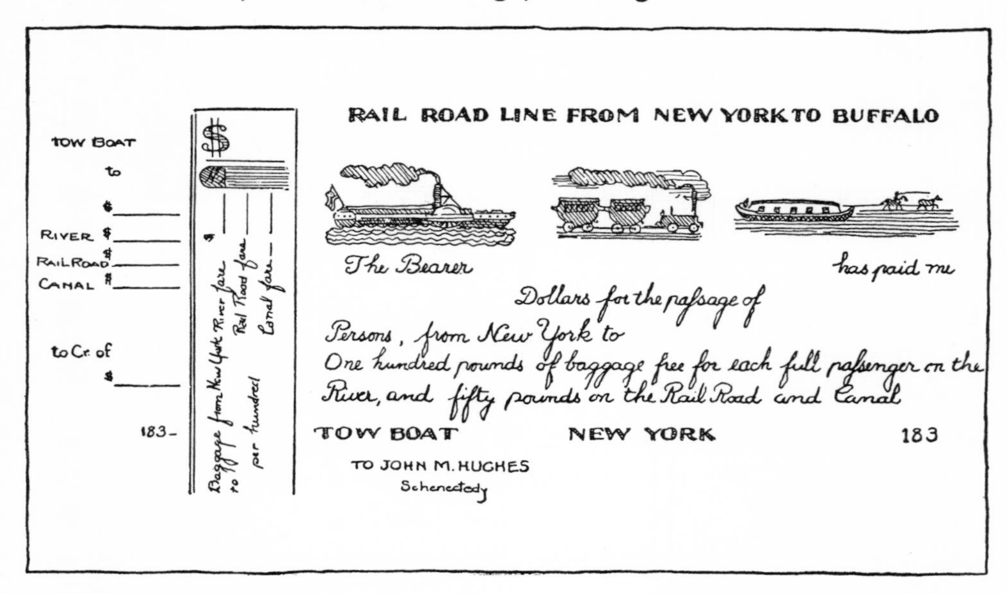

TOW BOAT
to
$
RIVER $
RAIL ROAD $
CANAL $
to Cr. of
$
183-

$
Baggage from New York River fare $
to per hundred Rail Road fare
Canal fare

RAIL ROAD LINE FROM NEW YORK TO BUFFALO

The Bearer has paid me
Dollars for the pafsage of
Persons, from New York to
One hundred pounds of baggage free for each full pafsenger on the River, and fifty pounds on the Rail Road and Canal

TOW BOAT NEW YORK 183

TO JOHN M. HUGHES
Schenectady

This is a picture of one of the first railroad tickets used in this country. The owner of this ticket took a steamboat up the Hudson to Albany, where he transferred to a train on the Mohawk and Hudson Railroad. This means that probably he traveled on the *Clermont* and that the *De Witt Clinton* pulled his train. At Schenectady the journey was continued by packet boat on the Erie Canal to Buffalo. Early railroad tickets were printed on large sheets of thin paper, or on small brightly colored pieces of cardboard. Sometimes small round pieces of metal, like coins, were used for tickets.

Oliver Evans' steam carriage.

The Clermont.

The Walk-in-the-Water.

The Savannah.

The race between the Cunarder and the Sovereign of the Seas.

Prairie schooner.

TRAVELING WEST

THE story of westward travel is one of the most thrilling chapters in the history of America. In this big country people were always moving farther and farther west, to make new homes for themselves. Wagons, large and small, jolted over the rough roads. Sometimes these were farm wagons with canvas-covered tops. Sometimes they were the big red and blue Conestoga wagons, the boat-like shape of which made them particularly useful for crossing rivers. Oxen were more often used than horses, they were stronger and more sure footed on bad roads. It was a long, tiresome journey that these white-topped "prairie schooners" took across the continent. There were endless hardships and the travelers were in constant danger from the Indians, who did not care to see the white man taking their land. One pioneer on the Oregon trail kept a careful diary. Some days he wrote very little, but the little he wrote told a great deal. Here are a few of the days from his diary:

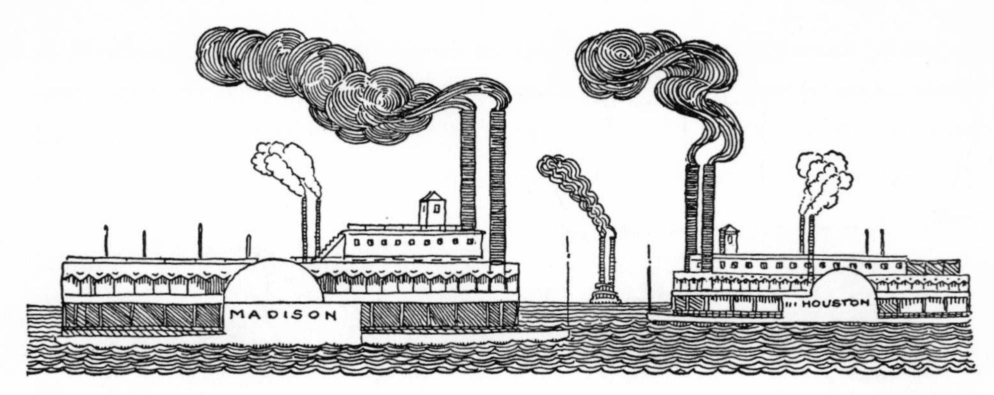

River boats.

June 22nd. We traveled sixteen miles to-day under a broiling sun and over a dusty road without finding a drop of water for our cattle.

July 12th. The dust is so deep as to cover our boot tops, and rises in such clouds as to prevent the driver from seeing his teams.

July 29th. In our day's travel I have counted near a hundred dead horses, thirty mules and sixty oxen; also about twenty wagons that emigrants have been compelled to leave.

It is easy to see why it took emigrants from four to six months to take the journey that an airplane can now make in a few hours. And it is easier still to see why some of them never got there at all.

Some westward travelers preferred to go to Pittsburgh and to build or hire a flatboat or ark on which they floated down the Ohio River. These boats were real homes on the water, just as the prairie schooners were homes on land, and people lived in them for months. There were small sleeping rooms, a living room, and a place for the animals—a cow, pigs, chickens. The boat was moved by a long sweep and only boatmen who knew the river could steer it past all the dangerous places. Travel on a flatboat was not always safe. There were rocks and shallow places, sunken trees and dangerous currents.

In early days river pirates lurked in caves along the banks. Still, it must have been a pleasanter way to travel than over land. On summer nights we can imagine an emigrant family sitting on the roof of the flatboat, listening to the music of a fiddle or to the boatman's song:

> "Hi-o away we go
> Floating down the river on the O-hi-o."

There were sailing boats on the rivers, too. After a time canals or artificial waterways were built. A great many people traveled on canal boats; the building of the Erie Canal meant a new and easier way to travel west. There were slow freight or "line" boats that carried some passengers and went at the rate of two and a half miles an hour. Fast packet boats could go about four miles an hour. If a man missed his boat he could hurry to the next bridge, wait for the boat to pass under it and jump on board! Sometimes passengers who were tired of sitting on the boat got off, walked on the towpath, and returned to the boat. The horses or mules that pulled the boats were changed every ten or fifteen miles. Small boats carried the horse that was resting; packet boats changed horses at regular stations.

It was pleasant to travel on a canal boat for there was no dust and passengers could sit on the flat roof and admire the changing scenery. At night it was not quite so pleasant, for passengers slept on hard shelves that let down from the walls. An English girl who traveled through Ohio and Indiana on a canal boat wrote an amusing description of her night in a top berth or shelf too short for her, and too narrow to allow for much moving around. She had to lie very still while "mosquitoes devoured" and "heat melted" her. Passenger travel by canal was so slow that it went out of fashion as the railroads came in. Canals, however, are still used for freight.

The coming of steam improved river travel. One night when the city of Louisville was asleep the people were startled by a noise such as they had never heard before. They sprang from their beds thinking that the end of the world had come. The noise was steam escaping from the exhaust pipe of one of Robert Fulton's first Ohio River steamboats! After that steamboats took possession of the Ohio and Mississippi rivers. At first everyone was surprised, Indians gathered on the banks to look at the strange "fire canoes." Soon, however, the steamboats with their tall black smokestacks became a common sight.

There were other ways of going west. The prancing horses of the overland stagecoach took passengers over the roads. Tall clipper ships made the dangerous voyage around Cape Horn, taking people and cargo from eastern ports to San Francisco. Then came a great change. A railroad was built across the continent. It was a wonderful day when the railroad built from East to West met the railroad from West to East. It was the end of a long, hard struggle, for the Indians made railroad building dangerous and difficult. The railroad builders also had to meet all the difficulties that the covered wagons had found—the desert, the mountains, the rivers. So when the railroads joined it is not surprising that there was a great celebration. The two locomotives steamed up to each other, the drivers shook hands and broke bottles of champagne over their engines. The way to the West was open!

The flatboat.

A canal boat.

The meeting of the East and West.

A motor tricycle

NEW WAYS TO TRAVEL

The Automobile

STEAM made great changes in our way of traveling.

Then came another great change in transportation—the automobile. It was fine to have steamboats and trains, but people had to get to the station or to the docks. Bicycles and horse-drawn vehicles could be used for short distances, but people were not really *mobile.*

The automobile really grew out of the bicycle, the wagon or carriage, and the development of the internal-combustion gasoline engine. The first successful internal combustion engines were made in France and Austria. In Germany, Karl Benz made motor tricycles. Gustave Daimler began with a motorcycle and also improved the internal combustion engine. France, too, was experimenting and gave us some of the words we use today. *Auto-mobile* was a "made-up" word, meaning self-propelled vehicle. *Garage* and *chauffeur* are both French words.

England had a special difficulty in developing the "motor car" as it has always been called in that country. There was a foolish law which said that a man carrying a red flag by day, or a lantern by night, must walk ahead of any self-propelled vehicle that ran through the streets. This law lasted until 1896.

In America many experiments were being made. The first successful internal-combustion automobile, using gasoline as a fuel, was made and driven in Springfield, Massachusetts, by Charles and Frank Duryea. Frank took it out at night so as not to frighten horses and pedestrians. It looked like a horseless carriage—and that is what the first automobiles were often called.

Riding in one of the first automobiles was as much of an adventure as riding on an early train. Their machinery was unreliable; so were their tires. No one knew just what might happen next, and if anything did happen there were no service stations to help the driver.

Roads were dusty or muddy, and people wore dust coats to protect their clothes and goggles to protect their eyes. The ladies wore veils to keep their hats on their heads, although the first cars were going only fifteen to twenty miles an hour.

Henry Ford, who lived in Dearborn and also in Detroit, was not the first to make an automobile, but he made one of the early ones. More important still, he was to make it possible, by using mass production, for more people to own a car. The first Ford car was strange-looking, with a buggy top and wheels of the bicycle type. Wherever Henry Ford left it standing, people gathered around and stared at it in surprise. People laughed at it, just as they had laughed at the first trains and steamboats. But everyone wanted to get in and try to run it. So Henry Ford had to carry a chain with him and fasten the little car to a post.

He called it his "quadricycle"—a bicycle with four wheels. His

The first Ford.

sister called it "Henry's little car." His wife was very brave about going riding in it and taking their baby boy along.

The manufacturers of different types of cars began to race them. In 1901 there was a race in Detroit, with a parade of a hundred cars in line. First came the electric cars, then the gasoline and steam-propelled cars. It was most exciting and people came in horse-drawn vehicles to see it.

Each type of car raced separately, and the gasoline cars made the best showing in the most important race. Henry Ford came in first in his little car. This was really due to the fact that of the two cars racing with him one withdrew before the race and one had a hotbox and lost speed.

Electric cars, then and later, proved to be slow. Steam cars, while they could be speedy, had other difficulties. They used kerosene for fuel, and this had to be lighted with a match, while other cars were started by an electric spark which ignited with fuel. The steam-driven cars also had to stop every forty miles or so to take on water.

These pioneer automobiles were most interesting. It is fun to look back at pictures of them. There are the Stanley twins in their Stanley Steamer, looking just alike, even to their beards. There is the gay little Oldsmobile called the "Curved Dash"—because its dashboard had a little style and was curved instead of being straight. This was the first car to be made in quantity, though not in large quantities as the Ford was later.

Old cars have now become valuable—like old furniture, they are antiques. Their owners belong to antique or vintage car clubs. You might some day happen to see a whole group of these cars coming at their slow pace along the road, all shined and polished by their proud owners. In some states there are special license plates for old cars, some with a picture of an early car! There are even races for these cars.

Detroit was a natural place to build up an automotive industry, because it was the center of the carriage industry. Also it was on a lake and cars could be easily shipped. Henry Ford started his company there, as did others. It is still the center of automobile manufacturing.

In 1908 Ford offered his famous Model T, which grew less and less expensive as more were made and methods were improved. At one time the Model T cost only about three hundred dollars, and many people could afford to buy one.

Automobiles were continually improved. By 1933 one car looked like the one below. It was not as streamlined as modern cars, and it still had wide fenders, and running boards to step out on. But it had a windshield, glass windows, and electric headlights—which early cars did not have. It also went a great deal faster. Roads had been improved, but new roads were needed as well as new laws for traffic speed and for better driver control. We are still building new roads and trying to get people to drive more carefully.

"Modern" in 1933

SPEED!

The Airplane

FROM very early days man has wanted to fly. As a Frenchman once said: "The sailing birds wear a happy look."

There were many attempts at flight, including the balloon, which could not be steered, then dirigible balloons, or airships, which could. In Europe and in America, around 1900, inventors were also struggling with the problem of how to make a heavier-than-air machine that would fly. Experiments with gliders proved that flying was possible. But gliders had no engines and depended upon air currents to keep them up.

After reading everything they could find, and experimenting in their bicycle shop and with gliders, Wilbur and Orville Wright of Dayton, Ohio, made the first heavier-than-air machine powered by a motor. The machine was a homemade affair with the cloth part of the wings sewed by the brothers on the family sewing machine, and it was powered by an automobile motor. There were rudders front and back to steer it.

This flying machine, not then called an airplane, was tried out by both Wilbur and Orville at Kitty Hawk in North Carolina. On its first trial it stayed in the air for twelve seconds. Later that day it stayed up for fifty-nine seconds.

There were no cheering crowds or excitement of any kind. The Wrights kept their experiments a secret. Only five men (including one Wright brother) and a boy watched the trial flights. It was a cold, windy day, December 17, 1903, an important date in the story of aviation.

The Wrights said that they hoped that their machine would make war impossible. Not much more than ten years later, the airplane went to war. This was World War I.

The first war planes took great courage to fly. They were flimsy little wooden crates, made partly of wood, with cloth wings, and they caught fire very easily. The pilots sat in open cockpits, with little protection from weather or from enemy gunfire.

During the war airplanes were developed and became more efficient.

The event that caught the imagination of America and of all the world was the solo flight from New York to Paris, made in 1927 by Charles Lindbergh in the little *Spirit of St. Louis.* We thought of little else during the thirty-four hours he was flying. Then, as the news came over the radio, we were suddenly all telling each other, "He's made it! That boy has made it!" When he came back to New York, Lindbergh had a hero's welcome. And because imagination and interest were so stirred, he did a great deal to make flying seem more possible to everyone. He wrote, "The year will surely come when passengers and mail fly every day from America to Europe." It did come. He also thought, "Planes may even replace automobiles some day, just as automobiles replaced horses. Possibly everyone will travel by air in another fifty years."

That has not happened yet, but in 1961 fifty years have not passed.

Thirty-four years after Lindbergh's flight, millions of people are traveling by airplane—but we still have automobiles, millions of them. We still have ocean liners, big and small, for those who think that a sea voyage is relaxing and that it is fun. The picture shows how an ocean liner looked in 1933. Now liners are more streamlined, though they do not travel very much faster. The S. S. "America" has held the "blue ribbon" for the speediest Atlantic crossing for a number of years, but speed records for ships do not mean so much in the days of air travel.

Trains are also still with us, though they have lost some of their passengers and freight to automobiles, buses, trucks, and planes. The picture that follows shows the "Twentieth Century Limited," which runs between New York and Chicago, as it looked in 1933, with its big black engine and its long plume of smoke. Now most trains are pulled by Diesel engines, and you cannot hear them give the wonderful long whistle that steam trains gave as they came near crossings and around curves.

Many people still like to travel by train and see cities and farms, deserts and mountains through the windows of a train as it goes along.

A great liner.

The Twentieth Century Limited.

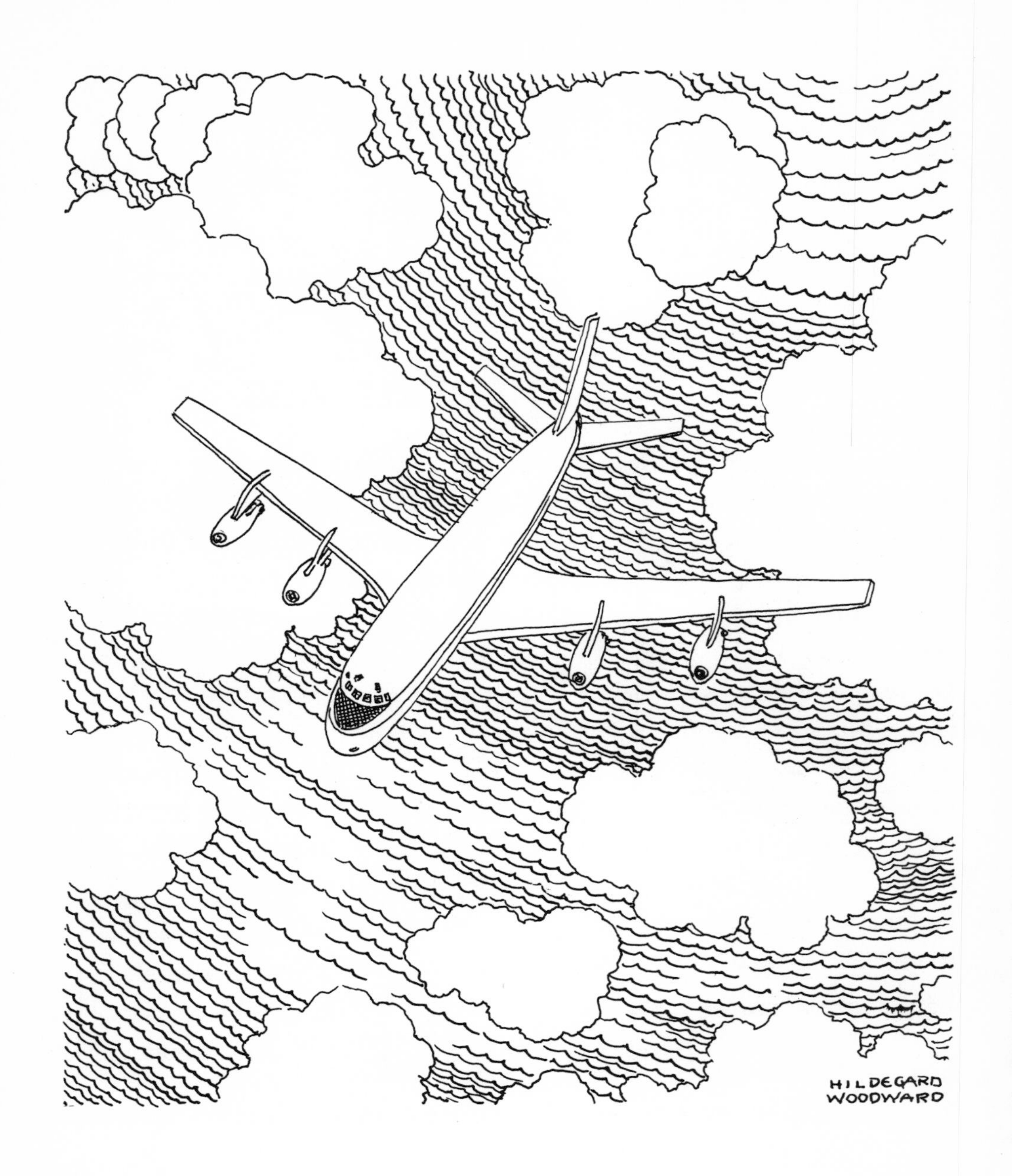
HILDEGARD
WOODWARD

JETS—AND THE SPACE AGE

As THE years have gone on, people are traveling farther and faster. You are children of the Space Age, so you know about jets and rockets. It seems to you as if they have been with us for quite a while. To grown-ups the time does not seem so long.

The principle of jet propulsion is not a new one, yet only toward the end of World War II did jet planes come into military use. Later, commercial jets arrived. We were not as surprised by them as people were by the early airships and airplanes. Then people had to get used to the idea that man was "up there with the birds," that he had really learned to fly and was able to control the direction of his flight. The change from the propeller airplane to the jet was not a whole new way of traveling—it was a matter of bigger, faster planes with a different type of engine. However, not so long ago, in each country that built jets, there was always a pilot who had to be the first to take a jet plane up into the air.

A pilot in Germany wrote of his experience in 1948 with the first jet. He saw a plane with the engines in pods under the wings—only two engines at that time. It seemed strange indeed to have no propeller. Then as he got into the cockpit and started the jet down the runway, he had the feeling that no runway could ever be long enough to get *this* plane into the air. But, as he came near the end of the runway, the jet lifted—and he was air-borne. "Then it seemed," he wrote, "as if angels were pushing me."

Propeller planes with piston-driven engines are still used for shorter distances, or travel between cities and towns that do not have airports at which a jet can be landed. There will also be more small jets for shorter distances. A big jet is expensive to build and expensive to fly, because it uses a great deal of fuel. Although the noise a jet makes as it takes off and lands has been muffled, people who live near airports still do not like it, and perhaps some way will be found to reduce this noise.

Travel has been made more comfortable for the passenger. All high-flying airplanes or jets are "pressurized." This means that passengers do not now have to use individual oxygen masks or tubes, as they once did. In 1941 I flew around South America, most of the time in that dependable plane, the DC-3. When we crossed the Andes between Chile and Argentina, we did not fly over the tops of the high mountains but through a pass between them. Sometimes passengers waited for several days to make this trip because the pass was full of clouds and the weather was not good. Going through the pass we flew at about 15,000 feet, and our oxygen supply came from a small tube by the side of each seat. Each passenger, as he began to feel the need of oxygen, put the end of the tube in his mouth. It was not as satisfactory as it might have been! Now pressurized jets make this flight, going *over* the high mountains.

In contrast, later in the trip I flew in the Boeing "Stratoliner"

Flying Cloud from Venezuela to the island of Trinidad. This was one of the first planes with a pressurized cabin—the pressure of air being kept as it would be at about 8,000 feet above sea level. We flew at 16,000 feet in smooth air, and it seemed quite wonderful after some of the rough flying that we had done at low altitudes. We did not see as much as we had seen when we were flying low. I was especially disappointed not to see the great river Amazon, because there were low clouds and we were above them. I was glad when the plane began to go down for its landing, and I could see the red roofs, the houses, and the flowering trees of the island.

Perhaps as you fly, some years later, you will see even less. We have Air Force supersonic planes that can fly one or more times the speed of sound. Commercial airlines are, as this is being written, meeting to discuss how soon the supersonic passenger airliner will be possible. They have found some difficulties.

First of all, as a plane passes the speed of sound it makes a "sonic boom" that travels along with it. The passengers on the plane do not hear the thunderclaps made by the plane as it breaks the pattern of the air waves. Those on earth do. Something will have to be done, if it is possible, about the sonic boom. You may have to wait a number of years to travel at higher altitudes and higher speeds. A passenger jet travels now at 500–600 miles an hour, and needs only about another hundred miles to pass the speed of sound.

But what will you see as you travel? Men discussing what can be done have suggested that supersonic passenger jets be made without windows. Then they decided that enough strong glass could be used to make very small windows, to keep passengers from feeling shut in. The pilot would probably have to do without windows and use a television screen.

There will be, as there is now, the problem of losing time in loading and unloading the plane, and that of losing time for passengers going from city to airport, and returning from airport to city. Perhaps the useful helicopter will be the answer. Several big cities already use helicopters to take passengers to and from airports.

In 1933, when this book was first written, there were no practical helicopters, although they had been planned and models had been made. The Wright brothers had a toy helicopter, when they were young boys, but they did not think in later years that a helicopter would work—they thought that if the motor stopped it would fall heavily to earth.

The autogiro came before the helicopter. It was invented in

Spain and had a propeller in front as well as the rotors that you see going round and round on today's "whirlybirds." We have helicopters because Igor Sikorsky, who came to this country from Russia, believed in them and built the first really practical ones. Others have made different types of helicopters.

Helicopters do not fly as high, nor go as fast, as airplanes and jets, but they can fly straight up or down, landing in a very small space. They can fly sideways and backwards and they can hover in the air without moving. If the motor should fail, the pressure of air will still move the rotors and the helicopter can glide safely to a landing.

The ability to do these things has made the helicopter most useful for rescue work on land or sea. A helicopter with pontoons or a boatlike hull can land on the water to rescue the crew from a boat that is in trouble. In a severe flood helicopters have hovered near third-story windows of houses and taken people to safety. Now some helicopters have jet engines.

Not everything is happening in the air, however. There are plans for a new way to travel—in a vehicle that will not have wheels and will almost fly. The railroads want to get back the passengers and freight that they have lost. The Ford Company has made a trial vehicle called the Levacar, which can float above railroad tracks on a thin cushion of air forced downward from the car. Railroads are considering trying this out. Between cities, on short runs, it should go much faster than present-day trains.

There are plans for a speedier crossing of the Atlantic, also. A hydrofoil vessel named the H.F. "Dennison" (H.F. for Hydrofoil Ship) will soon be launched by the Grumman Engineering Company. It is expected that the trip to Bermuda can be made in eight

hours, and that a larger vessel will be built to cross the Atlantic. As the object is speed, this ship will have hydrofoils or "water wings." With these, the hull, or main part of the boat, can rise up to six feet above the water. When the hull is raised, the drag, or resistance of the water, is lessened, just as the streamlining of a jet lessens the drag or resistance of the air. It is not a new idea—a hydrofoil vessel was tried out years ago by Alexander Graham Bell, the inventor of the telephone.

Our Navy has atomic-powered submarines and atomic-powered ships. Atomic-powered planes are still in the future. The advantage here is that atomic-powered vessels or planes can travel for a long time without refueling—and should also develop greater speeds.

In 1957 the Soviet Union surprised the world by putting Sputnik I, the first satellite launched from earth, into orbit. Since then, both the United States and the Soviet Union have sent up a number of satellites.

When one of the first balloons rose up into the sky from Paris, many years ago, its "passengers" were a sheep, a hen and a rooster. In some of the satellites, dogs, monkeys, and mice were the first space "passengers." Most of them returned safely to earth. They had proved that a living creature could survive a space flight.

Many questions remained unanswered. How would a man feel in space? As he came to zero gravity, and was outside the gravity or pull of the earth, he would be in free flight. This meant that his body would be weightless, and that, unless he was strapped into his seat, he would float around the cabin. Every movable object would float, too. Would he have a terrible feeling of loneliness up there in space? Astronauts, here and in the Soviet Union, went into training for possible space flights. Who would be the first to go?

This question was answered on April 12, 1961, an important date in world history. On that day Yuri Gagarin of the Soviet Union became the first man to go *outside* the earth's gravitational pull and to travel around earth in a space ship. This space ship was a large, heavy one, and a powerful rocket was used to propel it into orbit. Gagarin returned safely to tell something of his experience.

On May 5, 1961, an American astronaut made a voyage into space. His name was Alan Shepard, Jr., and the capsule in which he rode was named Freedom 7, because seven astronauts took part in the training program. It was boosted into space by a Redstone rocket.

This capsule did not go around the earth as did Gagarin's. But all America, and later all the world, could hear on radio or see on television what happened. Many of us followed the flight from the time when Commander Shepard put on his silver-colored space suit and walked to the rocket, to the time when he and the capsule parachuted into the ocean and were picked up by helicopter. And, as when Lindbergh made his famous flight, millions of Americans told each other, "He's made it!"

One of the astronauts in this training group, known as Project Mercury, will make a longer flight, perhaps in orbit around the earth. There are plans for space flights to the moon, though you will not be soon making visits there, as some books and stories have seemed to suggest.

What has happened is just a beginning. Whether or not it is possible for man to explore the moon and the planets remains to be seen. And all the future depends upon whether nations can live together in peace—on earth and in space.